The Saucer's ...

de Fontaine

0   25   50

Miles

F
O
R
N
I
A

Los Angeles

San Pedro

San Pedro

SANTA CATALINA I.
⑤

Channel

Gulf

of

SAN CLEMENTE I.
④ Santa Catalina

① La Jolla

② San Diego

San Diego Trough ③

O C E A N

MEXICO

Bahia Descanso

⑧

Exploring the

Ocean Depths

The Story of the Cousteau

Diving Saucer in the Pacific

Exploring the
Ocean Depths

The Story of the Cousteau

Diving Saucer in the Pacific

EDWARD H. SHENTON

W·W· NORTON & CO· INC·
NEW YORK

To Fred N. Spiess, of Scripps Institution of Ocean-ography, whose inspiration and foresight brought to-gether those scientists who used the Diving Saucer.

Table of Contents

1   Prelude   13

2   Preparation   23

3   Inside *La Soucoupe*   40

4   Men, Methods, and Missions   57

5   Scripps Canyon   67

6   San Clemente   87

7   On to Mexico   109

8   Cabo San Lucas Revisited   130

9   Noises in the Sea   162

10   April Showers in the Channel Islands   181

11   One Saucer and a Bag of Pelican Bones   198

Suggested Submersible Reading   205

Illustrations

Front View Cut Away of Diving Saucer
Rear View Cut Away of Diving Saucer
Chart of Diving Saucer Operations in the Pacific
PHOTOGRAPHS BETWEEN PAGES 94 AND 95

Acknowledgment

Project Diving Saucer '65 could not have come into being nor resulted in success without a great number of people who worked long and hard and foresaw the value of such a venture. So many people did so much to make our joint Scripps, Navy, OFRS, Westinghouse project a reality that it would be impossible to name them all. Thanks are due to Captain Cousteau, who supplied a remarkable team of men with the *Saucer*. André Laban, Raymond Kientzy, and "Gaston" Roux, who kept everything on the *Saucer* working, deserve great credit for their long hours and cooperation in making the scientists' dives successful.

From Scripps, Fred Spiess and Jerry Winterer coordinated the whole operation; Jeff Frautschy, Wic Burgeson, and Ed Price helped arrange all the contractual matters. At USNEL, Dr. G. H. Curl, Captain H. C. Mason, Dr. R. J. Christianson, and Dr. D. A. Wilson, supported by Dr. R. F. Dill and Commander J. Davies, were largely responsible for special equipment and diving arrangements.

The group at USNOTS who supported us at San Clemente Island were Bud Kunz, Howard Talkington, and Joe Berkich.

For PMR and NMC, Tom Henebry, Jim Moldenhauer, Gordon McCarty, and Lt. J. R. Elzenga were responsible for this series of dives being carried out successfully.

Finally, for the USNUSL, our dives could not have been made without help from Ray Hasse, Ken Moothart, Ralph Austin, and Ed April.

Certainly the impetus and reason for all our scientific dives and the formulation for a coherent program was due to the inspiration and efforts of each of the contributing scientists. Their names and experience are woven throughout the book; to each of them I am grateful for their sharing with me the details of their dives, which make the basis of the book.

Finally, to my fellow teammates whose time and devoted attention to the operation kept the project going while I interviewed divers and banged on the typewriter, I owe many thanks.

Exploring the

Ocean Depths

The Story of the Cousteau

Diving Saucer in the Pacific

CHAPTER 1

Prelude

The small loudspeaker rasped harshly, but the clipped message was drowned out by the pitched whine of the hydraulic pump as it came on. The pump switched off for a moment. The observer listened more closely, against other distracting background noises—the whir of the inverter and the hum of the jets. The two men in the *Diving Saucer* were surrounded on all sides by a complex array of instruments and machinery squeezed into the oblate spheroid that measured just over 6 feet in the major axis. In the darkness, the pilot lay stretched out on his stomach, along the left side of the cabin. He reached out with his right hand, knowing exactly where to find the switch just beneath his couch, and stopped the motor.

He lay quietly, waiting to hear the next words over the underwater "telephone." The observer on the other side also lay face down, but with his face pressed close to a 3-inch-diameter plexiglas port, intently watching a world outside flooded by powerful lights. Occasionally he spoke into a small microphone strapped close to the port, recording his observations on magnetic tape, which served as his notebook. The port framed a scene composed of pale greens mixed incongruously with brilliant reds, and magenta shot with splotches of yellow. These colors, surprising to observe in nature, represented the many thin growths of coral and corallines so profuse in some areas of the undersea world that they grow like luxuriant gardens. Under these encrusting tangles was the goal of many of the scientists—the rocks that eluded sampling devices, cameras, and dredges.

A distant-sounding voice came over the "telephone." The observer was reluctant to leave his vantage point, yet he knew it was time for the scheduled contact with the surface. He twisted his body around to his left slowly, so as not to upset the delicate balance of the craft, and reached for the gain-control knob of the set. The "telephone" was actually a radio that transmitted sonic energy through the water column. Over the years, it had earned the name "telephone" from the Navy, which used similar versions on submarines. But unlike the hardwire type that we are accustomed to using on land, our phone was a watery link. Many times a voice sounded miles away instead of a mere 1,000 feet. Now, as the observer adjusted the volume to minimize the background crackle, a voice came through quite clearly.

"*Soucoupe, Soucoupe,*" then repeating slowly, "*Soucoupe, Soucoupe,* this is *Shazam.* Do you read?"

There was a pause; the observer lifted the microphone from its cradle on the side of the set and, stretching it around so he could continue to see through the port, depressed the talk button. At the same time he quickly glanced at the depth gauge just inches from his left cheek, tilting his head at a strange angle to avoid parallax. The gauge read 210 meters, or exactly 672 feet below sea level.

"*Shazam, Shazam,* this is *Soucoupe* . . . Read you loud and clear . . . Do you hear me?"

This preamble, whereby communications were established every time it was necessary to do so, permitted the surface boat to move into the most favorable position for best reception, since the underwater communicating equipment was highly directional.

"*Soucoupe,* read you OK . . . come in and go ahead," said the watery voice.

"Our course is 070 degrees true . . . repeat . . . zero . . . seven . . . zero . . . true. Depth . . . 210 meters . . . two . . . one . . . zero meters. Temperature 10 degrees. We have collected some small samples from a large outcrop. Visibility near 20 meters. Some outcrops are 2 to 30 meters high. We will be coming up in twenty minutes . . . repeat, we will drop the weight in twenty minutes. Dive going well. Did you read?" The observer released the microphone button and heard the dull hiss of the receiver as he continued to gaze out of the port. A school of unusually bold and curious squid flitted so close that they almost touched the port. They always seemed to delight in darting into the bright lights. Before the observer could see them closely they would jet back into the blackness, with opalescent eyes reflecting the intense brightness of the headlights of the *Saucer.*

A few moments passed, then the return message filtered back into the small cabin, far from the warmth and light of the surface world. This time the voice was faint and less distinct. ". . . *zam.* Roger you . . . (static) . . . Standing by . . . " But this was nothing unusual, since toward the end of the conversation it was very easy for the surface boat to drift out of the cone of good transmission. As the angle between the *Saucer* and the surface increased, thermal layers refracted and bent the sonic signals and much of the message was lost. Underwater communication still presents problems that aren't easy to overcome.

The other end of this conversation was coming from the surface tracking boat, which had earned the name *Shazam* early in our operation one gray and chilly evening off the bleak, windswept island of San Clemente—but that story will come later. I was with *Shazam* on this particular morning.

About every thirty minutes the *Diving Saucer* was expected to check in on the telephone and report the progress of the dive. Many times it annoyed the scientists to have to communicate while they were making valuable observations—but it was necessary for the surface crew to know that all was well. In some cases this communication provided a means of recording certain data that might otherwise be forgotten in the excitement of seeing new things, perhaps for the first time, in the sea. Further, these checks were a good way to keep tab on the location of our undersea craft.

While the tiny, yellow, oval-shaped vehicle crept somewhere below, we in the surface crew were trying our best to keep track of its progress by a very crude acoustical method that had the same failings as the underwater telephone, in that sound waves were bent by thermal layers of the sea. Two or three of us would bob around in the 17-foot skiff *Shazam*, listening with a small movable transducer we placed in the water to pick up the steady pinging noise emitted from the *Saucer*. Our tracking system used this "pinger" on the *Saucer*, which gave a signal or a beep about once a second. Our transducer or "receiver" on the surface could usually pick it up. With some guesswork and a bit of training we were sometimes able to follow the track of the *Saucer* within a hundred feet as it explored along the bottom and up steep submarine valleys. The communication was less successful when our scientist/passenger and the pilot glided gently between narrow canyon walls or sneaked under an overhanging precipice. Then the acoustic signal would bounce deceptively on the wall or be lost completely before it reached the surface. At such times we found ourselves chasing misleading echoes back and forth across steep gullies unseen beneath us. On many days, however, if the bottom was smooth and without sharp features, and if surface conditions were calm, we might drift lazily along. Yet on the other hand, we might find ourselves being carried unfavorably by strong winds or currents and always having to move on to hold station over the *Saucer*. For those who took turns tracking in *Shazam* there was usually time for collecting thoughts, meditating, or a chance to chat with some of the scientists who went along to help on the topside part of this exercise.

This particular day was turning out to be one of those drifting times when we seemed to stay directly over the *Saucer* and have no trouble in communicating. Our boat rolled easily, with the long smooth Pacific swells building up several miles off shore. The bare, sparse hills visible from our boat were that dull brown common to Southern California. The tops of the hills were crisply outlined against the sky, like a stage backdrop, in contrast to the remembered softer hues of the eastern seaboard with its higher humidity. The mid-morning warmth of the sun was pleasant and nearly put me to sleep— we had been up since 5:30 that morning.

Now, as the dive proceeded, the time to drop the ascent weight approached. Time went so fast—all the scientists seemed to react the same way. They had become so engrossed in their work that they completely lost track of time.

The *Saucer* cruised slowly along a few meters off the bottom. Occasional patches of dark rock contrasted with the lighter sand that shone even brighter in the glare of the powerful headlights. Some of the rock at this depth was encrusted with marine growth, although not as heavily as the rocks nearer the surface. The covering on the rocks and mounds took on unusual brilliance as the intensity of the lights increased close by, showing deep red and orange, then rich tones of purple and brown. The combined pattern of the colors resembled nothing ever seen in nature on land. The *Saucer*'s rate of progress over the bottom was slightly over one-half knot, very slow in this era of high speed. But there was so much to see and to assimilate. While moving within only several feet of all this scenery the scientist had to decide whether to photograph possible good examples of geological or biological conditions. Actually, the speed of the *Saucer* was adequate for the amount of detailed observation required. Everywhere there was marine life happily at work and play in their black and cold water world. Sometimes the crew came on an area literally teeming with tiny crabs no bigger than the end of one's little finger—all busily scurrying about on apparently important missions. A swarm of large shrimp loomed into view as the pilot flicked on the bright lights. These creatures swayed and pranced gently and rhythmically over a muddy bottom on long, delicate legs that never sank into the soft ooze sediment. So large a mass of shrimp is considered unusual, so documentary pictures were in order. The scientist controlled the still camera and would snap two or three sets of pictures with 35mm color film. At the same time, movies were being made to record the conditions. Often the pilot operated the movie camera, since he was more familiar with the positioning of the *Saucer* and could get better coverage. If the scientist insisted on being his own movie cameraman, he had to ask the pilot to switch on the "cinema" lamp. In the sudden excitement of a rare find, many a scientist has shot valuable footage of movie film forgetting to use the 2,500-watt incandescent light that gives the correct color-balanced light intensity to the scenes. To further enhance the quality of the movies taken, the designers had placed the cinema lamp on a hydraulically controlled boom that would extend the light beyond the *Saucer* to attempt to eliminate the effects from light backscatter and turbidity of particles. This boom could extend the light nearly 5 feet from the *Saucer*.

The occupants of *La Soucoupe* (as the *Saucer* was called in French) finished filming, retracted the lamp, switched it off, and began to head deeper over a steepening slope. They were at 260 meters and getting near the 300-meter depth limitation. The scientist urged the pilot on down this steep sediment slope, but the latter firmly shook his head, saying they must go up. For a moment the scientist was alarmed—was something wrong? In the dim glow of the small instrument panel he saw the pilot reach under the couch and twist the lever that mechanically released the 55-pound iron ascent weight carried outside the pressure hull. The scientist glanced at the depth gauge, then noticed the adjacent clock—it was 1430 already! Those last twenty minutes had whisked by. The two men had been in their confining and protecting shell for exactly four hours from the time they left the surface.

The French pilots were exacting about the duration of each

dive. Some scientists found themselves slowly departing from their fascinating world right on schedule, much to their displeasure, for they could happily have gone on for hours. The pilots, realizing how engrossed some scientists became, had set four hours as a safe, arbitrary limit, although the life support system would normally operate for nearly six times this period of submersion. Prolonged use of the propulsion jets as well as the headlights and powerful cinema lamp drew heavily on the batteries and limited dives to four hours. Another of the many safety factors built into this remarkable vehicle was a surfacing system that operated independently from the electrical system. It was not uncommon for the *Saucer* to surface with the batteries totally expended. Unlike other submersibles, which require a certain reservoir of power, the *Saucer* depends solely on dropping weight to return to the surface rather than on blowing tanks or exerting propulsion.

Now, slowly, the *Saucer* began to rise from the sandy bottom on its return ride to the world above water. The pilot sat up and reached across the scientist, who was now reclining on one arm watching the depth gauge. He flipped on the sonar and switched to the upward-looking transducer to measure the distance to the surface. It was still too far for the instrument, which was limited to 200 meters, so he turned to the down-looking transducer, which showed a slanting trace on the recording paper indicating that they were rising normally —probably about 50 feet per minute. Ascending in the darkness with no point of reference was a strange sensation, with no feeling of motion. If one of the low-powered lights was switched on, it was usually easy to see particles in the water that appeared to be falling. This is what is called "snow"; it can be used as a good movement indicator both vertically and horizontally.

As soon as the up-looking sonar transducer was turned on, the pilot knew that the surface crew in the tracking boat could hear them clearly. Although the small pinger kept emitting a signal throughout the entire dive, when the *Saucer* was on its way back, the upward sonar had a characteristic pitch. *Shazam's* crew normally listened to the pinger with a parabolic reflector placed in the water. The pingers, made and supplied by the Navy Electronics Laboratory, were 5-inch-long cylinders with a battery in one end and transmitter in the other. The seawater acted as a conductor between the two ends and the pinger continued to beep once a second. In this way, the surface boat could track the course of the *Saucer* along the bottom. Many of the scientists wanted to know their approximate location and the path of progress of the dive. The object of the tracking boat was to stay directly over the *Saucer*—or where the *Saucer* was thought to be as indicated by the pinger. Then either the ship could plot this location as a relative bearing and range or the tracking boat could take "cuts"—horizontal angles on known shore points.

At about 200 meters, the *Saucer* occupants could begin to see considerable light filtering from the surface, if the lights were all off. The farther from shore, the better the water clarity. One scientist exclaimed that he could have read a newspaper at 200 meters' depth, which is extremely clear for light penetration. The visibility at such times might range up to 60 or 70 feet.

The "snow" continued to fall and the sonar showed a steady and even rise slanting up the recording paper at about 45°. During the slow ride up, the scientist took periodic checks on the temperature and any observations of layers of plankton or material in the water column. The outside water temperature was measured by a thermistor mounted on the current meter. The water at 200 meters was about 10° Centigrade. During most of the year, the surface water in this part of the Pacific doesn't warm up much and readings of 12° or 13° C. on the surface are common. At the end of the summer, temperatures of 18° to 20° C. occurred, causing greater stratification. The scientist kept a sharp watch for any thermal boundary signs. As they approached the upper layers, cloudy areas or concentrations of particles frequently indicated a boundary, which also showed up on the temperature probe, where the warmer water rested on the slightly cooler water. This boundary, under more severe conditions, was responsible for distorting sound paths. It was, of course, this discontinuity that permitted submarines to lie undetected by searching destroyers during World War II, since the sound waves were bent unpredictably. For those in the *Soucoupe* this stratification—or thermocline as it is known by oceanographers—only served to make underwater communication difficult.

The *Saucer* was now approaching 100 meters and rising steadily. The light intensity increased noticeably. As it passed 30 meters, the water became warmer and the *Saucer* picked up speed slightly. The light in the water was brilliant and sparkling; a school of fish reflected orange and silver in the clear water some 40 feet distant. With an almost imperceptible change in motion, the craft broke onto the surface. From the ports it was easy to see the surface disturbance and the bubbles churning from wave action. The pilot sat back and looked up through one of the two small top ports that gave 120-degree vision. He then reached to his left side and moved the controls that hydraulically rotated the two water jets straight up. At the same time he turned on the propulsion motor, and outside two streams of water shot up in the air some 10 or 12 feet to mark the *Saucer*'s location.

This technique had always been used by the French pilots to aid in locating the *Soucoupe* after a dive. Even after we added a citizens band (CB) radio and tracked the *Saucer* closely, the pilot gave a blast on the jets for good measure.

Inside, the two saucernauts lay comfortably. Their mission was completed. The scientist penciled some notes in a small book. The pilot rewound the magnetic tape on which all the observations during the dive had been recorded through an open microphone. Faintly they could hear the rush of water as the two-foot waves splashed on the top of the *Saucer*. The next familiar sound that signaled the beginning of the recovery operation was a loud clank as the bridle ring was placed on the center of the hatch by the diver dispatched from the mother ship. Soon they saw a flipper dangling down in front of the port as the hookup diver attached the three legs of the bridle, each with a large shackle that fastened to the lifting lugs of the *Saucer*'s steel hull. In four minutes there was a slight jerk and suddenly the two undersea explorers were plucked out of their watery environment into the brilliant daylight, and effortlessly swung toward the mother ship.

To view all the activity on the deck as the *Saucer* is lifted aboard out of the water and yet hear nothing is a strange sensation. The ¾-inch steel hull acts as effective sound proofing. But as soon as the *Saucer* comes to rest in the cradle, like a giant egg in a nest, all the ship's noises and engine vibrations are transmitted clearly through the hull. More clanking, shackles to be undone—then a rap-rap on the hatch. The pilot reached up and spun the hatch lock and the 15¾-inch-diameter hatch sprung open with the help of the hookup diver who, grinning, wiped off the few remaining drops of water around the hatch and welcomed the saucernauts back. The dive was over. For the scientist it was merely the beginning of much work to assemble the new data that might change old theories. For the *Diving Saucer* it marked one of over 400 dives accomplished in six years of very eventful life.

CHAPTER 2

Preparation

The Underseas Division of Westinghouse Electric Corporation had been developing and producing torpedoes for many years. So it was a natural step from torpedoes to a manned submersible which could carry out underseas exploration. The original plan was for the completion by 1963 of a small, three-man vehicle that could descend to mid-depths of the oceans.

The venture was a collaboration of Westinghouse and the Office of French Undersea Research (OFRS), directed by Captain Jacques-Yves Cousteau. Captain Cousteau was convinced that scientific understanding of the seas was possible only by actual human observation, eventually at all depths. He agreed to build a diving craft based on the principles of his successful diving saucer, *Soucoupe,* and Westinghouse proposed to operate such a submersible for underwater research.

The construction of the vehicle—named *Deepstar*—in France progressed slowly. Lack of adequate knowledge of pressure-resistant materials for the hull caused most of the delay. Techniques for welding high-tensile steel had not been fully developed. Neither in France nor the United States had engineers conducted sufficient testing to predict the behavior of the welded metal under severe pressures.

By 1963 it became evident that a different material for the spherical hull must be found. Any hope for an operational submersible appeared to be a year or two away.

At this point, a decision was made to use a steel about which a known technology existed. The Underseas Division of Westinghouse selected HY-80, a metal similar to that used in Navy submarines. A pressure sphere was successfully constructed at the beginning of 1964.

Meanwhile a small but active group of scientists on the West Coast had been watching the development of research submersibles and with experience gained in using the bathyscaphe *Trieste I* began to develop programs of undersea exploration and research. Many of these men were eager to use other submersibles as a new tool in the oceans. *Deepstar* had been anticipated for sometime. Where was there another submersible? *Trieste I* was now scrap. *Trieste II* was fully committed to the *Thresher* search off Boston. A few other small submersibles existed in this country, but they were capable of diving only to several-hundred-foot depths.

It suddenly occurred to Tom Horton of the Underseas marketing group one day late in 1963 that there was a ready solution.

"Why not bring the Cousteau *Diving Saucer* from France to this country? We could give many of the scientists a short dive and show them how to use a submersible in their work. Furthermore, it might give us a first-hand idea about the market potential."

The idea was favorably received and shortly afterwards Captain Cousteau agreed by telephone to send the *Saucer* to California in January of 1964.

And so the *Diving Saucer* came to this country on a month's lease from Cousteau. Some 57 dives were accomplished, showing interested scientists the promise of undersea vehicles. The *Saucer*'s capability of diving to 1,000-foot depths exceeded anything operational in this country and it had already achieved some 145 dives since 1959.

The series of successful dives off Southern California played a major part in the formation of Project Diving Saucer 1965. Following the return of the *Saucer* and the crew to France it had become clear at Westinghouse that *Deepstar* was still more than a year distant. We had hoped for a vehicle to be available not too long after the first dives with the *Saucer*. Interest on the part of scientists from the Scripps Institution of Oceanography and the Navy Electronics Laboratory was now tuned to a high pitch. Money for a diving program existed.

By late spring Tom Horton and other Westinghouse officials saw clearly that the time was right to lease the *Saucer* again. They pressed ahead to make arrangements to bring it back for a longer stay and a working contract. It looked like a four-month program involving many of the participants from the first series of dives. Scripps and the Navy Electronics Laboratory were the prime users and had spent the greatest amount of time in developing methods and tools for use with the *Saucer* in order to extend their knowledge into deeper water off the California coast. Dr. Fred Spiess of Scripps had sparked the interest among the geological and biological groups who now wanted to make use of this new and promising technology.

In the Underseas Division preparation for Project Diving Saucer was stepped up. The operational team was being hired by early summer of 1964. Planning for support equipment was under way. Selection of the equipment was often governed by the possibility of carrying it over to the *Deepstar* operation, and most of the handling gear was to be designed to serve both vehicles rather than the *Saucer* alone.

By July our plans were firm. Westinghouse would lease the *Diving Saucer* from Cousteau for at least four months beginning in November, at a time when he could not operate in the stormy Mediterranean. The *Saucer* and a French pilot and mechanic would fly to California and join a ship with a six-man Westinghouse crew. We would then proceed to provide our "customer"—a group of scientists and engineers—with a minimum of 15 dives each month at various sites along the coast. This project would be the first of its kind—a very specialized diving service for undersea scientists.

Our six-man operating team had been hired over a period of several months. The men represented a variety of previous experience related to a planned submersible diving service.

First to join the project was our supervisor, Charles F. (Fred) Willett, who held a Master's degree in geodesy. He had recently retired from the Navy, after twenty years of service, much of it in marine survey and shipboard hydrography. His task was to coordinate supplies, the support vessel, and the *Saucer* in California. He had taken part in the first *Saucer* project in January 1964 and was fully qualified to head this second operation. His knowledge of the necessary logistics was a solid foundation for future operations.

Jared Burnett had been with Westinghouse Field Engineering and Service for five years. In January 1964 he was assigned to the first *Saucer* project to assist the French team that had been sent by Captain Cousteau. Jerry had liked the work. He transferred to the Engineering Department and became one of the original *Deepstar* team. He came from New York State and had gone to the University of Miami, where he studied electrical engineering. With Westinghouse he had worked on radar installations. At 28 he was the most experienced member of the team, especially in maintenance of the electrical system, a vital function.

Joseph A. Thompson was a mechanical engineer and expert photographer. Thirty-five years old, he had spent a great deal of time in underwater photography. He had lived close to the New Jersey coast, where he had gained experience in diving and photographing wrecks of ships. His skill was a valuable addition to the team. He also wanted to become a submersible pilot.

Arthur L. Somers came to Westinghouse through its graduate training program. Larry had received his college degree in Business Administration but his real interest turned toward the sea. He joined the Navy after graduating and served six years as an officer in Explosive Ordnance Disposal (EOD). He was a specialist in salvage and handling bombs and weapons. As are all EOD officers, he had been thoroughly trained in diving, both "hard-hat"—helmet and suit—and scuba.

The youngest member of our team, Valentine Boelcskevy was a physicist from the University of West Virginia. Val was born in Hungary but was educated in this country. He had designed a number of ingenious instruments for underwater use and, like most of us, was an experienced scuba diver.

I was the last to join the *Saucer* team. My graduate work had been in marine geology and oceanography, including research and survey projects at sea over the previous ten years. Since Westinghouse anticipated that much of the *Saucer* diving would be for marine geologists, it was logical to have someone with such a background to coordinate these scientific activities.

When finally complete, the *Saucer* team represented a well-rounded combination of talents. Fred Willett directed the at-sea operational part. Joe Thompson and Larry Somers were to be pilot trainees. Jerry Burnett was responsible for maintenance of the *Saucer's* electrical systems. Val Boelcskevy planned the instrument requirement, while I was in charge of liaison with the scientists who were to use the *Saucer* for their various explorations of the ocean canyons off the California coast.

As part of the preparation for pilot training, Joe and Larry were sent to Marseilles, France, for six weeks with the French pilots of the *Diving Saucer.*

The final stages of preparation for Project Diving Saucer were going on in Baltimore. The guiding principle behind our operation was that it should be easily movable from one ship to another. Our attention was then turned to the three living and four workshop vans being built by a local trailer manufacturer there. We had selected vans similar to those used in the house-trailer industry. Ours were adapted to shipboard use and could be welded to the deck of the mother ship. Two of the living-quarter vans were 24 feet long by 8 feet wide, one 30 by 8, including an office and library area. Bunks and locker space were provided for six men in each van. Since we expected eventually to be working in both hot and cool climates, the living areas were heated and air conditioned.

The work vans were smaller, measuring 8 feet on a side. Two of them had specially built-in benches and shelves for electronic and mechanical shop work, repair, and service for the *Diving Saucer*. We intended to be as self-supporting and independent as possible while at sea.

While this construction proceeded, we managed to get a support ship to meet our needs. A 136-foot ship, the *Burch Tide*, used mostly in the Gulf of Mexico to run supplies, mud, and cement to the offshore drilling rigs, was offered to us by a ship-chartering company. She was ideally suited, giving us ample deck space, which measured slightly less than 100 feet long by 27 feet across. This would allow our vans to be placed aboard—and still leave space for the *Saucer* and its handling crane on the stern. Although the idea of putting vans aboard ship was not totally new, it was the first time that a submersible vehicle and living quarters had been carried on a ship as a completely portable unit able to go anywhere the ship could take it. Captain Cousteau, of course, had led the way by carrying the *Diving Saucer* aboard his 136-foot research ship *Calypso*, a converted mine sweeper, which he had made famous through his worldwide oceanographic expeditions. Our concept differed in that we expected to be able to move our entire facility from one ship to another as work might demand. There were many similar ships of this particular 136-foot class used by oil companies throughout the world. If our operation grew, as we hoped it would, we could expect to move it about frequently.

Fred Willett consulted with Tidewater Marine about structural details on the ship and the reinforcements necessary to mount our heavy crane on the stern. Concurrently, we searched for a good recording echo sounder for the ship that would give us accurate depth measurements in the shallow ranges where we expected to be diving with the *Saucer,* and at the same time serve as an adequate instrument for occasional surveying in deeper water. The one we found had a range of up to 2,000 fathoms—considerably beyond our immediate needs but well suited to the requirements of our own projected submersible, *Deepstar,* which was designed to dive to over 4,000 feet.

Much of the material procured for Project Diving Saucer over the next six months was similarly affected by future considerations. On the first *Diving Saucer* experiment in California we had used a 5-ton earth scoop for a crane on the support ship. While it managed to place the *Saucer* in the water and retrieve it each time, it was strained to near capacity in rough weather. Fred Willett had managed the handling technique in that operation; for the present one he decided that we should have the largest stock crane available and one that could be used later for *Deepstar.* After much searching he found one that amply met our requirements. It was a back hoe intended for construction excavation work. The crane looked monstrous in the pictures, which showed enormous hydraulic pistons and a boom that dwarfed the operator. It didn't look very seagoing to me, and the thought of this contraption on the stern of the ship seemed almost ridiculous. I had spent a fair amount of time aboard oceanographic ships and had always taken a dim view of putting landlubber's equipment on them. Accustomed to working with winches specially designed and built for the oceanographer, I was dubious about a stock land item adapted to a rugged at-sea application. During the next six months I was to see how wrong I had been on this score.

Around the first of September several of us flew out to La Jolla to meet with our principal customer, Scripps Institution of Oceanography (SIO). Scripps had agreed to act as central coordinator for the other laboratories involved in leasing the *Diving Saucer.* Representatives from all these groups attended the meeting at which we from Westinghouse and Scripps discussed the necessary arrangements for bringing the *Saucer* from France, getting French nationals into this country as pilots and mechanics, placing instrumentation aboard the *Saucer*, and many other details.

Our other customers were the U.S. Navy Electronics Laboratory (NEL), also in San Diego; U.S. Naval Ordnance Test Station at Pasadena, California (NOTS); U.S. Navy Underwater Sound Laboratory (USL), New London, Connecticut; U.S. Naval Missile Center and Pacific Missile Range, both of Point Mugu, California. Each of these organizations had a series of dives planned with a particular mission in mind. SIO had scheduled the majority of dives for their scientists. As it looked at this time, there was to be a minimum of 90 dives and a possibility, if all went well, of 115.

Scripps and NEL agreed to provide most of the specialized instrumentation. This included temperature probes, current meter, underwater telephone, pingers, and surface tracking gear. If there were any requirements beyond this basic complement, each participating laboratory would have to build or provide its own equipment for particular experiments. Westinghouse had wanted to build some of the special instrumentation, but at the time we were fully engaged in getting our part of the support facility assembled. The Underwater Sound Laboratory had already begun the design for an acoustic array it wished to place on the *Saucer* sometime in February 1965. Their purpose for using a vehicle like ours was to make measurements of background or ambient noise in the sea. The *Saucer* appeared to be a quiet platform and had no cables or connections to the surface that could introduce unwanted interference. Other laboratories had less definite plans or were more involved in merely observing from the *Saucer* instead of investigating specific engineering applications.

At the meeting we determined to begin the diving series for Scripps on November 1. The operations team planned to leave from Baltimore on October 15. Each member had decided to bring his family along, except Fred Willet, who had several children in school and college.

The pace began to pick up in Baltimore as we started shipping tools, basic *Saucer* supplies, and other support gear to go aboard the ship. This included expendable iron ballast weights cast for us in California; a type of transformer oil that filled the battery cases, thus compensating for pressure; bara-lyme, the absorbent of carbon dioxide removed from the cabin during a dive; a small bench lathe and hand tools, electronic supplies, and basic test equipment; and many other pieces we had determined from the first *Saucer* experience.

Our two prospective pilots, Joe and Larry, returned from France, where they had observed the *Saucer* in action aboard the *Calypso* in the Mediterranean. They answered many of our questions about specific details of the *Saucer*.

I had found very soon that one of my greatest problems in talking to the various potential customers was the fact that I had little real understanding of the inner workings of the *Diving Saucer*. What few drawings we had were old, unrevised, and out of date. Jerry Burnett knew that most of the original circuits, hull penetrations, and exterior connections had been changed several times since the 1959 assembly drawings were made at the time the *Saucer* was built. All the wiring schematics were, of course, in French. It took time for us to get them translated into English and then we always had to be careful that millimeters were properly converted to inches or that some other vital bit was not lost in the translation. Every time I tried to lay out a prospective program involving the *Saucer* and some special gear that a scientist or engineer wanted to take to the bottom the most elementary questions would stump me. What was the length of the mechanical arm, what arc did it describe, and what weight could it grasp? The answers to some of these questions had to wait until we actually had the *Saucer*. In the meantime we made educated guesses and hoped for the best.

One of my projects involved collecting and assembling a library of references and textbooks covering the geology and oceanography of the areas where we would be diving. It was a good refresher for me to comb through the stacks in the geology library at Johns Hopkins to find a representative number of basic papers and articles on Southern California marine geology.

Larry Somers was elected our Diving Officer since he had

had considerable experience while he was with the Navy. He had spent a tour of duty on an aircraft carrier as an EOD officer. All of us had some diving experience. Joe Thompson had spent a lot of time over the past 15 years in undersea photography; others of us had done mostly sport diving. Nevertheless all of us passed physical and proficiency tests to qualify as divers should we be asked to dive for the company. Each man was equipped with all the necessary scuba gear and we bought a large and dependable air compressor to enable us to recharge diving tanks quickly.

Joe Thompson became our official photographer and equipped himself with the necessary underwater cameras for 16mm movies and 35mm still photography. He chose a Bolex 16mm movie camera with a 10mm wide-angle lens in an underwater housing made by the manufacturer. For still photography he preferred the Rolei-marine with a 120 film format, a Minolta SR-7 for surface 35mm use, and a Nikonos 35mm submersible camera. It was the bare minimum for undertaking the documentation of our operation, and we later bought a Bronica S-2, which gave us better underwater still photography.

It was almost the first of October and soon we would be heading west on our long trek to California. Before going, we decided to try out some of our new equipment. I knew of a perfect spot—an old quarry I had worked in previously that had clear water and depths of at least 70 feet. It was near Harper's Ferry, West Virginia.

The weekend weather turned out fine and crisp, but warm in the waning sun. We met near the quarry and drove our cars down a steep hillside on a winding dirt path that led through the fragrant apple orchards. The branches had been propped up to keep from breaking under their enormous loads of fruit.

The quarry lay hidden in a patch of woods. While the wives sunned on blankets and the children romped near the water, we pulled on our new wet suits and waded into the cool, clear water to try out the new scuba equipment. We had bought good equipment. We had chosen single hose regulators of the best quality and added the See-view gauge, which lets one see how much air (by pressure) remains in the tank. In addition, all our tanks had the reserve air supply, called a "J" valve, which most believe to be an added safety feature. But many so-called safety features can be a detriment if not carefully checked. Many a diver has inadvertently knocked his air reserve "on" at the start of a dive and found to his dismay that there was no reserve supply when he needed it. The air gauge was thus a dependable way of keeping watch on the air remaining in the tank.

We helped each other put on the tanks as we balanced on the steep slope of the quarry. It always takes longer than one expects to get into a suit and tank, adjust the straps, fit the back-pack, get knife, depth gauge, watch, weight belt, life vest all properly strapped on. Larry and I went off together. After standing in our suits in the sun the cool water felt pleasant. We dropped to 30 feet easily, clearing our ears with that familiar squeak and pop—first one, then the other. At 40 feet the water was noticeably cold—about 45° F. Joe took along the 16mm Bolex movie camera in its new underwater housing. Larry and I had the *Calypso* camera to try out. We sank quickly—too quickly, in fact. Both of us had put too much weight on our belts for the new suits. Joe, with the heavy movie camera, was worse off than I. We saw him briefly disappear in a dark cloud of black ooze and silt on the bottom. Then he tried to swim up, but he was too heavy. All hope of photography was gone now, for the bottom was well stirred up. Larry and I exchanged grins underwater as Joe finally parted with his weight belt to ascend. We had been accustomed to diving in the ocean, where the salt added more buoyancy, and we had put on too much weight. Together with the decreased density in the sharply colder water we had considerable negative buoyancy. We suspected also that perhaps our new suits had fewer air bubbles in the foam. Of course, as a diver goes deeper the foam compresses, giving less buoyancy. That is why divers who plan to dive deep take less weight and merely have to work a little harder near the surface. We swam up with some difficulty but no panic.

Back on shore, we took a break for lunch. In the midst of the picnic, a man drove up and stopped. I recognized the farmer who owned the quarry and surrounding orchards. He announced that we would have to leave at once—no skin divers were allowed here. Skin diving was excluded from the insurance coverage on his quarry. Tom Horton went over to explain to the farmer who we were. Tom was a most able persuader. He told about the Westinghouse program, our *Diving Saucer* venture, Captain Cousteau, our individual achievements as highly trained professional divers, until the farmer's eyes grew wide with amazement. It was all true, but Tom had glorified the story as only a skilled salesman can. He wound up his pitch by pointing at Larry and relating his feats as a Navy diver and said, with some reverence, "This guy has a worldwide Navy diving ticket!"

This last was too much for the farmer. He weakened and allowed us to remain, provided we didn't let any other divers come in that afternoon. As he drove off, we congratulated Tom. There was no such thing as a "worldwide Navy diving ticket," but it certainly sounded impressive.

During the next week, the remaining shipments were sent to the West Coast. Our household goods, which we held to a minimum, were placed in the storage and work vans just before shipment. Joe and I decided to take along our motor bikes. We thought we might even put them aboard the ship when the operation moved to Mexico, so that we could use them as local transportation.

On Tuesday, October 1, the Gulf Coast, especially along the Louisiana shore, was hit by a severe hurricane. The storm damaged many marine facilities and held up the departure of the *Burch Tide* for California. Now it was impossible for the ship to get to Long Beach in time. Fred Willett hurriedly made arrangements for the use of a smaller ship, *Hugh Tide*, for the first month's operations, while *Burch Tide* was overhauled, brought through the Panama Canal, and up the coast to California in late November. The *Hugh Tide* measured 101 feet and would be adequate for the first month of *Saucer* activities since we expected to dive locally off La Jolla and would not require the more extensive living quarters of the vans. We could get along with one work van and no living vans; the ship slept 21 persons below.

While the storm raged along the Gulf Coast, we took stock and found that all our preparatory projects had been completed and, in fact, very little was left to be done except for loading our own cars. Jerry Burnett had already started West in order to get his wife settled before he flew to France. He was to accompany the *Saucer* aboard the cargo transport plane scheduled to arrive at Long Beach in late October.

Meanwhile, the rest of us decided to visit some of the other research groups about to launch themselves into the deep new world of undersea exploration by submarine. We arranged to inspect the nearly completed and long-awaited *Aluminaut* in Connecticut, and the smaller new vehicle, *Alvin,* which was undergoing tests at Woods Hole, Massachusetts.

Aluminaut was conceived by Reynolds International Inc. as a bold venture, using heavy aluminum rings or sections to form a submersible nearly 50 feet long. It was built by the Electric Boat Company in Groton, Connecticut. The official launching ceremonies had been held in September 1964; now, in October, builders were making last-minute adjustments and installing some of the large and complicated navigational and scientific equipment. Among the gigantic nuclear submarines of the Navy, the *Aluminaut* looked small. But to us, whose *Diving Saucer* wasn't even 10 feet at its greatest dimension, even *Aluminaut* loomed large. All 86 tons of it sat squarely on the construction pier, the faint afternoon sun highlighting its glossy blue and red body. Accustomed to many visitors and the accompanying tracked-in dirt, the engineer-in-charge issued each of us white coveralls and canvas shoes like the ones worn in clean rooms associated with the aerospace industry. We walked around a scaffolding to the bow. The nose section had been removed. One by one we filed through a small forward hatch. A long corridor extended to the dimly lit stern section—it seemed much longer than 50 feet. The only other submersible I had worked with had an over-all length of 18 feet and an 8-foot-long pressure compartment. The *Aluminaut* was packed with racks of electronic equipment. Technicians stood working at the installation of some of it. We gawked at everything—TV screens, monitors, consoles and control stations, the large seat for the pilot, pumps, batteries, fans, and containers. The whole thing reminded me of a prop for a popular television show. The *Aluminaut* was a work of careful design and planning carried out by people who specialized in building submarines.

Outside we were shown the ballast system and the propulsion and steering mechanisms. Our guide told us that *Aluminaut* had been given six coats of epoxy paint—each a different color—in order that scratch penetrations or corrosion could be determined for best maintenance of the aluminum. It was extremely important that the aluminum be protected from seawater and effects of stress corrosion. We made notes on many of the design features, for the day when we might be involved in the operation of a craft this size. As an operational team our greatest interest centered on the proposed techniques of handling such a vehicle. Its enormous battery capacity gave it a long operating duration range so that it could travel, if necessary, under its own power to the diving site. If the diving site was far offshore, as is the case on most of the East Coast, much valuable power would be consumed in surface transit before diving. On the other hand, *Aluminaut* could be towed to the site, as were the bathyscaphs *Trieste I* and *II*. But this, too, presented problems, because the towing speed is slow and hampered by rough seas. The other principal alternative involves taking the submersible aboard a support ship and then proceeding to the diving area. But, considering the 86-ton weight of a vehicle such as the *Aluminaut*, this requires some very special handling and lifting equipment.

Time would tell just how this large and complex submersible could contribute to aiding man in the exploration of the underseas areas. As we stood there admiring the craft and discussing it, with its potential diving capability of 15,000 feet, I became aware for the first time of being a part of a small group of adventurers who might some day routinely live and work at these depths in the oceans. Even though the *Diving Saucer* was limited to the upper 1,000 feet of the sea, the idea persisted that we were on the edge of an unvisited realm. On later occasions in our experiences with the *Diving Saucer,* I realized that our present efforts and equipment would soon seem very crude and primitive, just as the early flying machines were superseded by the rapid development of more complex aircraft.

Woods Hole is one of the most concentrated areas of oceanography in this country. In several blocks of modern laboratories and offices three organizations, with over 500 employees, turn out important volumes of oceanographic data and analyses. Woods Hole Oceanographic Institution is perhaps the best known of the three and has done as much to advance the science and knowledge of the sea as any organization in oceanographic research. The other Woods Hole organizations are the U.S. Fish and Wildlife Service of the Bureau of Commercial Fisheries, and the Marine Biological Laboratory. WHOI, as the Woods Hole Oceanographic Institution is known by most oceanographers, is a privately funded organization, unlike the majority of the other research groups, which are associated with universities and colleges. WHOI is a leader in the oceanographic fraternity on the East Coast, and its activities are worldwide.

The growing interest in the use of a submersible had, over several years, culminated in Allyn Vines's concept of *Alvin.* *Alvin* is a three-man submersible built by General Mills (now a part of Litton Industries). This vehicle, the first of its kind conceived and built in the United States, was designed to dive to 6,000 feet. The project was financed by the Office of Naval Research and *Alvin* was to be operated by WHOI for the Navy.

Alvin's pressure hull was formed from HY-100 steel into a sphere some 7 feet in diameter. The rest of the vehicle, including batteries, propulsion, ballast tanks, and flotation, was built on and outside of the 2-inch-thick hull. Our own *Deepstar* had a similar basic design, although it differed in some of the systems, such as propulsion and ballasting.

Alvin was launched in June 1964 and was undergoing trials and pilot training when we saw her. The *Alvin* group was about a year ahead of *Deepstar*.

On this raw October day, several of us went first to visit with old friends who had worked with *Alvin* for some time. We were welcomed with cups of hot coffee in their cozy, slightly Victorian office over the local drugstore.

Dr. Earl Hayes, Director of the *Alvin* group, explained to us that his men had been conducting a number of shallow dives in the local waters to a maximum of 70 feet to check the performance, maneuverability, turning radius, and speed of *Alvin*. "We hope to complete this series in the next few weeks and, after some modifications, we'll head for deeper waters down south for the final sea trials," he said. "I'm sorry we don't have better weather for your visit, but if you want to watch the day's operation, we can lend you foul-weather gear." It had begun to rain as I looked out the window to where Dr. Hayes was pointing out the activity on the dock. "All our dives have been staged right off the dock there, using the large 'cherry picker' to put *Alvin* in the water," he continued. "The tender follows along as the pilot drives her across the harbor to the diving site."

We left the building and made our way over the bridge and out on the dock at the "Oceanographic." *Alvin* sat on its own low cradle, a part of the outer fairing, looking much as I had expected on the basis of the sketches and few pictures that had appeared in technical magazines. It was painted white and stood a good 12 feet high, with a large "sail" or conning tower forward. Several of the technicians were working around it, checking seals, removing fiberglas panels, and climbing in and out to make adjustments. It was certainly quite a different craft from what I knew the *Diving Saucer* to be. It weighed perhaps 13 tons as opposed to the *Saucer's* 4 tons and was several times the *Saucer's* vertical size.

During that wet day we had a good opportunity to watch the operation of this vehicle as well as to get to know several of the Woods Hole team members. Larry and Joe both rode in the vehicle and observed it in action. Later, the rest of us went aboard to study the inside layout, instrumentation, and control console. *Alvin* had a diver in attendance who cheerfully paddled about in the cold water. Our own system for the launch and retrieval of the *Diving Saucer* involved a diver who most of the time acted merely as a swimmer but occasionally went below for special missions. Each of us shivered a little watching the WHOI diver cavort in the 50-degree water, but since we were all trained scuba divers, we knew that he was quite warm in his protective wet suit. In fact, we were probably colder on that drizzly day than our diver friend.

The day at WHOI had been quite enjoyable despite the weather. We had experienced a valuable camaraderie in the exchange of ideas between the two operational crews. And we had seen two quite different types of submersible—both of considerable merit. *Aluminaut,* an example of the first of the larger submersibles, represented the first venture capital invested by industry in what was believed to have a huge potential. It was a radical departure from all previous designs and was built of a wholly untried material for deep submergence. The workmanship seemed excellent. Little of what we saw had any relation to our future activities with the *Diving Saucer,* for these were vastly different boats. On the other hand, the harbor trials of *Alvin* revealed to us possible problems we might encounter when we received *Deepstar.* As for our immediate situation—that of operating a diving business with the *Saucer*—few analogous lessons could be gathered by watching the *Alvin* operations.

CHAPTER 3

Inside La Soucoupe

Jacques-Yves Cousteau has probably done more than any other one person over the past 25 years to encourage and lead his fellow man into the sea. He is one of the undersea pioneers and believes firmly that mankind has an unlimited future in the "mother sea." Cousteau may be compared to an earlier maritime explorer, Henry the Navigator, who during the fifteenth century led and inspired the exploration of more than half the globe by men of his own and ensuing generations.

Cousteau, with the help of Emil Gagnan, developed and patented the aqualung in 1940—a tool that has brought the beauty of marine life and the undersea environment to countless thousands of persons. The aqualung has permitted man to venture routinely to 200-foot depths to explore, to perform tasks, and to enlarge his knowledge of the sea. It uses a demand regulator to supply compressed air from a cylinder containing about 70 cubic feet at about 2,000 pounds pressure per square inch. Thereby the diver breathes freely air at a pressure equal to that around him and is unaffected by this pressure since all air-filled spaces in his body are filled or compensated. The use of this device has certain severe limitations. The harmful effects of the partial pressures of nitrogen and oxygen at greater depths can cause so-called nitrogen narcosis and oxygen poisoning and are well known by divers. While some divers go deeper than 250 feet, such a depth is considered by most the maximum for effective undersea work or exploration. The air supply varies inversely with depth, allowing the diver only a few minutes' stay at over 200 feet and may require decompression upon return to eliminate excess nitrogen in the system. Excellent health is an absolute requisite. The physiological complications resulting from deep diving have plunged even the best divers into trouble, and in some cases have resulted in death. In many localities, sharp thermal layers are encountered and the diver finds himself in cold and dark water, a factor that contributes to limiting the length and safety of the dive.

The recent perfection of new breathing apparatus now allows man to inhabit greater depths. Based on the experience of Navy "hard-hat" divers using a mixture of helium and oxygen, this equipment regulates the mixture of gases for divers tethered on hoses to a chamber at depths up to 600 feet. By eliminating nitrogen and substituting an inert gas like helium the diver can avoid the disabling and "narcotic" effect of nitrogen and the harmful toxic effect of oxygen. Nevertheless, the technology of saturation diving and mixed gases has become more complex and is beyond the realm of all but the highly trained professional diver.

During the early 1950's, when the aqualung was just being introduced in some quantity to this country, Captain Cousteau and his explorers were diving to great depths—even in excess of 300 feet. They observed the animal life, poked into caves, and investigated wrecks. On deep dives they experienced cold and nitrogen narcosis or "rapture of the depths."

In addition to the diving experiments, Captain Cousteau was carrying out research programs with R/V *Calypso*, making a number of worldwide cruises to collect data and make observations. It was about this time that he saw that there was a real need for man to work in the sea as well as on it. In *The Living Sea* he relates the experience of a frustrating ten days spent amid raging seas and winds trying to emplant a buoy:

> As my men fought on the tossing work-deck to recover the last [camera] sled, I stood on the port bridge wing, squinting into the falling sun, the gale whistling in my ears, and reviewed our tribulations. In ten days' battle for a few photos, I had burst a winch drum, towed a camera that didn't work, got myself anchored involuntarily, spent hours paying out the hauling cables, lost a balloon and 59,000 feet of nylon, and been prevented from setting a radar target [reflector] by a silly squid. I swore in the teeth of the wind that I was going to cut my way out of this web of cables and abandon the tormenting surface of the sea. I was more certain than ever that exploring of the deep was the job of men in scientific submarines.

Several years went by before Captain Cousteau's dream had a chance to take shape. Initial work began on the submersible vehicle idea as early as 1955 at l'Office Français de Recherches Sous-Marine (OFRS), one of his groups located in Marseille, France. Cousteau laid down the basic parameters to Jean Mollard, Chief Designer, and André Laban, Director of OFRS. The vehicle was to be primarily an extension of a scuba diver to permit the explorer greater depths for a longer time with more safety and comfort. Like a diver, the observer was to have good visibility and the ability to take photographs and obtain hand samples. Above all, the device had to have the maneuverability of a diver.

The design took the shape of a flattened sphere for the pressure hull. This permitted two observers to lie prone looking through viewing ports. As much of the machinery and equipment as possible was placed outside in the seawater where the greatest advantage of flotation could be achieved.

Thus, the heavy batteries, propulsion unit, and attitude control were put outside the pressure hull and covered only with a fiberglas shield. The ellipsoid hull measured 6.5 feet at maximum diameter and was formed of two halves of ¾-inch-thick mild steel welded together. Openings or penetrations in the hull included the two conical viewing ports 6½ inches maximum diameter, three small wide-angle optical windows around the top, a movie camera port, and eight hydraulic lines and electrical control connections. No pressure testing facility existed in 1957 that could accommodate a hull of this size; the pressure testing was therefore carried out in the sea, as is still done with larger vehicles, such as *Aluminaut.* The selected operating depth of *La Soucoupe Plongeante* was 1,000 feet or, in the measure of oceanographers, 300 meters. This first hull was further referred to as DS-1 for *Diving Saucer*-1. The tests were conducted from the *Calypso* at Cassis, France, near the site of research work carried on previously by OFRS. The first set of deep dives was tethered and unmanned and the bare hull was ballasted with a section of chain and other gear to compensate for the buoyancy of the hull. Normally, of course, the additional machinery makes this compensation. The test depth used was 3,000 feet, giving a safety factor of 3-to-1—far in excess of the usual submarine design criterion, which is in the vicinity of 1.5-to-1 or less. This safety factor was typical of much of the *Soucoupe*—it reflected a conservative approach that was incorporated in all of the vehicle's systems. During our operations with the *Diving Saucer* we came to appreciate the reasons for its being built as it was.

During the test, DS-1 was suspended by a cable and lowered to nearly 3,000 feet from the deck of the *Calypso* to test it under pressure. Everything was going well until it neared the surface during the recovery. A sudden motion of the ship caused a great strain on the suspending cable and the small yellow hull broke free, sinking back into the depths. It came to rest in 3,300 feet of water, where it was plainly visible on the ship's echo-sounder recorder, which showed it to be some 15 feet off the bottom, hovering, neutrally buoyant, above the length of chain. This was a great blow to the plans of

Cousteau and OFRS, and again demonstrated the treachery of that small area—the air-sea interface. Yet over the next several years, the hull of DS-1 endured, and each time the *Calypso* went by her people would "see" it in its position as it was shown by the echo sounder—true proof of the sound design and fabrication of the *Soucoupe* hull. This misfortune is one of many that forced Captain Cousteau to remark later, "You can trust a cable to do one of two things at sea—either get fouled or break."

Nearly two years passed before DS-2, the present and only existing *Soucoupe*, was produced and readied for its sea trials. Cousteau and his men from OFRS worked hard to put DS-2 through the required tests. As is true of any other prototype working in a totally new environment, all progress was real pioneering. Some of the more frustrating problems occurred with the batteries. The power supply of DS-2 was originally a set of nickel-cadmium batteries that offered a tremendous power-to-weight advantage. This was considered important, since propulsion, lighting, and maneuvering are all dependent on the main batteries. Wisely, the designers had decided that ascent and return to the surface must be independent of power. Thus, while the battery life determined many important functions, the safe return (and also the descent) are accomplished by releasing weights. During the early test dives, the nickel-cadmium or Nicad batteries malfunctioned and began to explode, rocking the small craft violently. The 400-pound emergency ascent weight got its first test at this critical time. The *Soucoupe* and its occupants shot quickly and safely to the surface. The designers then worked on a better battery case and returned to the conventional lead-acid batteries, feeling that the nickel-cadmium type was not fully developed for undersea applications. The protective cases for the lead-acid batteries were quite simple and rugged, and most important, they worked perfectly in 1959 and continue to perform today. Each battery case is about 2 feet long by 1 foot across. The individual cells are placed inside, filled with electrolyte, and then the case is filled with a nonconducting transformer-type oil. A plexiglas cover in a flattened pyramid shape is bolted on and the oil filled near the top. Each of the six cases has a one-way relief valve that allows any gas that accumulates to escape—but keeps seawater out. As the pressure outside increases, bladders underneath, also filled with oil, are pressed, forcing more oil into the case—thus compensating for the pressure at any depth. After each dive, more oil may be added, since some is expelled on the dive. This system has had far fewer problems than would be the case if the batteries were placed in pressure-proof housings. The difficulty with batteries in pressure cases is that the gases given off have to be vented. If the vent system fails the case may explode. In the oil-compensated case gas can freely bubble out of the valve.

This battery case was only one of the many unusual and effective solutions the Frenchmen devised to get their interesting craft successfully underneath the sea. There were numerous thrilling experiences on the first dives before *La Soucoupe* was considered operational. Several of these are related in Captain Cousteau's book, *The Living Sea*. From 1960 to 1964 the *Diving Saucer* engaged in some 130 dives for Cousteau and other scientists in various programs in the Mediterranean.

Looking at the *Diving Saucer* in greater detail, let us consider the boat in general, and then examine in turn each one of its systems.

The extreme over-all measurement is 9½ feet from wing tip to wing tip—that is, if you can call the fiberglas housings for the jets by the aircraft term "wings." The mere presence of jets on a submarine is strange enough. The fact that the *Saucer* is less than 10 feet over-all means that it is air transportable—an important feature in a portable operation. The pressure hull, in the shape of an ellipsoid, is 79 inches in diameter by 60 inches in height. With the addition of the cradle it is nearly 84 inches high. This height can be trimmed slightly for accommodation on some aircraft. In operation trim the *Soucoupe* weighs in at a shade over 8,000 pounds. One of the most common reactions when people first saw it was amazement at its small size. When you come right up to it, it does seem very small, yet at the same time the inside impressed me as being larger than I had expected, for there was ample room to sit up comfortably. The cutaway drawings on pages 48–49 show the general layout.

Systems and Other Specifications

PROPULSION

The *Saucer's* propulsion uses a jet system but since it works in the medium of the sea, water squirts out of the two nozzles to move the vehicle along. A 2-HP electric motor in a pressure case drives a water pump through a divider, called the "Y," along two hard plastic 2-inch tubes around each side to the jet nozzles. The flow of water can be directed to one side or the other or allowed to flow equally by a hydraulically controlled ram that performs the function of a rudder. The jets are mounted on the wings with the rack-and-pinion movement permitting the jet to rotate 270 degrees from straight forward around counterclockwise to straight down. This control is also hydraulic and is one of the three principal controls on the pilot's left side. The jets can be rotated in unison or separately, as in a twin-engined motor boat. This maneuver of opposing the jets causes an immediate rotation of the *Saucer* about its axis. The center of the propulsion system is the electric motor, which is sealed in a pressure-proof container. The coupling from the motor to the pump is cleverly engineered with an oil seal that prevents any leakage. The motor is operated at two speeds—half and full—and is controlled by the pilot on a control console. The speeds attainable with this system are understandably slow—since pumping water in this manner does not realize a high efficiency. Full speed is less than a knot—1.1 mph. But the *Saucer* was not designed as a transport vehicle to cover large distances quickly over the bottom—it was, in fact, built to allow man to explore and inspect the features of the bottom in detail. Speeds in excess of 1 knot would frequently be wasted by the requirement to cruise close to interesting features slowly enough to turn, twist, and maneuver into narrow gullies and submarine canyons.

The requirement for greater speed presents the design engineer with immediate complications of more power, increased weight, and subsequent reduced endurance. Thus, the *Diving Saucer* designers chose a route that favors slow speed and high maneuverability. Many of the newer submersibles reflect the desire to cruise farther and faster—but still use relatively conventional propulsion. All submersibles have had to make the same compromise; they have had to sacrifice some maneuverability and have taken on greatly increased weight or size or both. Although many feel that the speed of the *Saucer* and its resulting range of 2-to-3 miles is highly limiting, numerous biologists and some geologists with whom I have talked strongly urged against greater speeds, for it was all they could do to observe, classify, and photograph areas at less than 1-knot speed.

BALLAST

One of the strong safety factors incorporated by Captain Cousteau in his vehicles is the ability to drop weight instead of using power for descent and ascent. The submersible, unlike the true submarine, does not employ ballast tanks and compressed air to blow them for ascent. Instead, either by dropping weight or by expelling ballast water, the submersible can come to the surface. The *Soucoupe* uses an effective and simple system of two 55-pound cast-iron weights mounted just below the observation ports. These are held in place on the bottom by two pins and on the top by a movable pin connected to a mechanical penetration in the hull. A lever inside is turned left or right 45 degrees to release first one of these pins—to establish neutral buoyancy—then the other, for ascent. When the *Saucer* is launched with these two weights in place, it is approximately 55 pounds heavy, causing descent at about 60 feet per minute. When the bottom is in sight or shows 15 meters or so away on the echo sounder, the pilot releases the first weight. The *Saucer* is then almost neutrally buoyant and fine adjustments are made by taking in small amounts of water into a 12-gallon tank or pumping out similar amounts. The water enters a surge tank at ambient pressure and

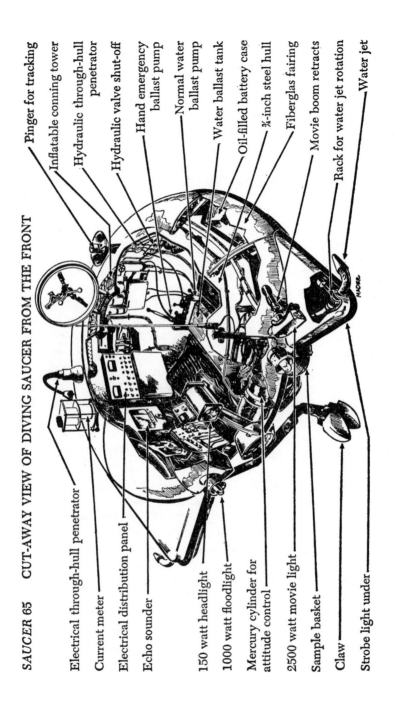

SAUCER 65   CUT-AWAY VIEW OF DIVING SAUCER FROM THE FRONT

Pinger for tracking

Inflatable conning tower

Hydraulic through-hull penetrator

Hydraulic valve shut-off

Hand emergency ballast pump

Normal water ballast pump

Water ballast tank

Oil-filled battery case

¾-inch steel hull

Fiberglas fairing

Movie boom retracts

Rack for water jet rotation

Water jet

Electrical through-hull penetrator

Current meter

Electrical distribution panel

Echo sounder

150 watt headlight

1000 watt floodlight

Mercury cylinder for attitude control

2500 watt movie light

Sample basket

Claw

Strobe light under

SAUCER 65   CUT-AWAY VIEW OF DIVING SAUCER FROM THE REAR

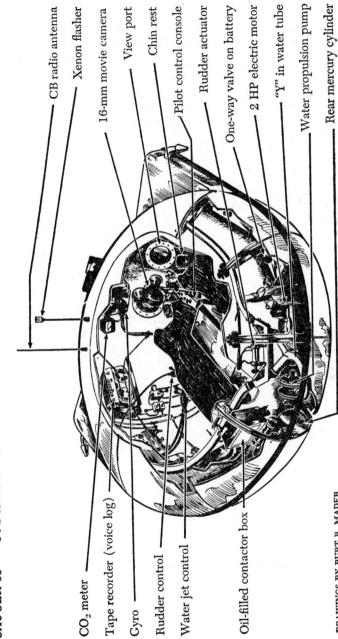

CB radio antenna
Xenon flasher
16-mm movie camera
View port
Chin rest
Pilot control console
Rudder actuator
One-way valve on battery
2 HP electric motor
"Y" in water tube
Water propulsion pump
Rear mercury cylinder

CO_2 meter
Tape recorder (voice log)
Gyro
Rudder control
Water jet control
Oil-filled contactor box

DRAWINGS BY BURT B. MADER

the pressure is reduced as it flows into the tank. An electric pump expels the water while a hand pump stands by in case of electrical failure. The emergency weight is part of the ballast system, although it is not routinely used. It is molded of lead and is situated on the lower aft portion of the *Saucer*. This 400-pound weight is released by a mechanically rotating shaft similar to that of the other weights, with a lever inside that must be rotated nearly 360 degrees to prevent accidental release.

HYDRAULICS

The majority of functions on the *Soucoupe* are performed by hydraulic actuation. The system is located inside the hull where a motor-driven pump maintains a 1,000-pound-per-square-inch pressure. Like the water emergency pump, there is a hand-operated hydraulic pump should the power fail. The system has a reservoir, which is a tank with an open vent inside the cabin. Each time a hydraulic control is used, the pump operates to maintain pressure in the system. Hydraulic actuators control the rotation of the two propulsion jets, the "rudder," the vehicle attitude, the mechanical arm, and the cinema lamp boom. These controls can be adjusted from inside and all lines may be closed off from the inside by valves. This latter fact is important if leakage develops in any line.

ATTITUDE (PITCH)

The *Saucer* must allow the occupants to look up or down, or move up or down slopes itself. There are 275 pounds of mercury contained in two cylinders located fore and aft—the forward one is above the center line, the aft one below, so that if all the weight of mercury is in one, say the bow, there will be a down angle of 30 degrees. The mercury can be shifted in about ten seconds from fore to aft to change attitude. The pilot uses a small lever located under his berth that hydraulically forces the mercury from one cylinder to the other. The mercury can be dumped overboard in case of emergency to provide the *Saucer* with about 250 pounds additional buoyancy.

LIFE SUPPORT

A 20-cubic-foot tank of medical breathing oxygen is located under the observer berth. A valve bleeds oxygen into the cabin and a flowmeter shows the rate. This tank contains enough to support two persons for about 24 hours, while 16 pounds of baralyme are used to absorb the carbon dioxide expelled. The granular baralyme is put into six perforated trays placed throughout the cabin where it can best absorb the CO_2. A barometer shows the cabin pressure, to enable the pilot to maintain the interior within several pounds of one atmosphere. If the pressure increases, he decreases the oxygen flow until a near normal pressure is obtained. A fan circulates the air to keep the CO_2 from concentrating at the bottom of the cabin. A second fan blows air on the ports to prevent fogging. A carbon-dioxide measuring meter is used to sample the atmosphere to determine the percentage of CO_2 and note any buildup that could affect the respiration and comfort of the saucernauts. A second bottle of oxygen was added during our operation to extend life support to a total of 48 hours.

BATTERIES

Six lead-acid batteries located on the exterior around the center line supply 105 ampere-hours of 120-volt power for propulsion and lighting. This supply allows a normal dive of four hours. The batteries take about 15 hours or overnight for a full recharge. Depending on the combination of use cycles and total hours, the batteries have a life of up to 100 dives of normal operation.

INSTRUMENTATION

Navigation. An air-driven gyrocompass similar to the ones used in small aircraft gives the pilot the information to steer a particular course. The depth of the *Saucer* is measured by a pressure gauge of the bourdon type, which reads to the closest 10 meters. A check against this reading is obtained from the echo sounder, which can "look" both up to the surface or down to the bottom and in addition can provide a paper record of the whole dive for later reference. This sonar also looks ahead up to 200 meters to measure distances. A tape recorder with open microphones for pilot and scientist records observations, instrument readings, and serves as the log of the dive.

Cameras. The Edgerton 35mm still camera in a pressure-protected case is mounted on the exterior. Two lenses give a fixed focus of 1-meter and 3-meter distances, while a 400-watt second synchronized high-intensity strobe light provides adequate lighting. A 100-foot roll of film provides 410 frames for each dive. Between the operators is a movie camera mounted inside that films 16mm sequences through an optical port. Up to 1,000 feet of film can be loaded, although in actual practice 400-foot reels are best suited.

Lights. Two main headlights illuminate the water with 1,650 watts while other smaller ones offer 200 watts and 150 watts respectively for lesser requirements. A 2,500-watt specially designed lamp lights the immediate area for the movie camera. This lamp is hydraulically extended on a boom out to 5 feet from the *Saucer* to avoid light backscatter. Finally, the lighting department is completed with a 1-watt second 240,000 lumen xenon flasher which is used for night identification and recovery on the surface.

Other Instrumentation. Several other important instruments were installed. These were built or purchased by several of the laboratories who chartered the *Saucer*. The current meter was a Savonious-type rotor that registered both speed from 0 to 1.5 knots and distance traveled in meters. A temperature sensor showed the water temperature in degrees Centigrade. Communication underwater was accomplished by a 42-KC telephone that gives a dependable link from the surface to the *Saucer* below.

During the beginning years of her life, the *Diving Saucer* was referred to as "Denise," but somewhere along the way this name was dropped and the less specific *Soucoupe* or *Saucer* became preferred. The *Saucer* had picked up many additional names as time went on. Gaston, the French mainten-

ance chief from OFRS, one day when I was first getting to
know him said in his halting but correct English, "We call
Soucoupe 'Fromage.' It is like a big yellow cheese and when
everyone is working in it, they look like little mice climbing in
and out." "Fromage" never stuck as a name for the *Saucer,*
but it was one of the more amusing descriptions.

As with other ships or yachts where the owner is always
eager to show visitors around above and below, we too liked
to take newcomers on a miniature expedition of the *Saucer's*
insides. The true amount of interior space in the *Saucer* is
quite difficult to photograph and depict because of its circular
shape. It is far better appreciated if one actually goes inside.

Some of the more agile members of our team could leap
gently onto the step points on the port side of the *Saucer* that
led to its hatch, while the rest of us and the visitors entered
more sedately by the stepladder tied alongside. The hatch is
only 15¾ inches in diameter, which at first sounds a bit re-
strictive—but we found that it accommodated some people of
ample girth. As you lower yourself through the hatch, your
feet touch down on the metal water-ballast tank that lies between the two berths or couches. You then squat down and
move over on one knee onto the starboard couch designed for
the observer. "Careful with your feet," I would caution as the
visitor or new observer began to stretch his feet back. "Mind
the fan blades and the electrical board there." There was a
place where feet went as one lay on the couch looking out the
starboard port. "You can rest your chin on that small, round
foam cushion," I told each new observer, "and from there you
can see out the port; look to the left and you'll see the depth
gauge; a few inches back is the current meter and temperature display. On your right side is the panel for the strobe
flash and 35mm frame counter." At this point, the observer
has to twist around to see things on his right and make a
mental note of these positions, since it will be dark inside on
the dive, and he must remember the number of exposures remaining on the Edgerton camera. Next, I show him where the
camera firing buttons are. "Down on your left side just below
the edge of the couch is the still-camera button. Each time

you fire it the strobe will flash. Remember to wait 12 or 15 seconds between shots—the flash unit takes that long to fully recharge. Also, keep in mind the focal length of the two lenses—1 and 3 meters." We found out after a while that much of this information could be written out in advance for orientation. "The movie-camera button is just to the other side—right here—but before you shoot be sure that the pilot knows what you want to shoot and he can then position the *Saucer*, turn on the bright movie light, and follow through with the sequence." Good movies require skill to take and many of the scientists left most of this routine to the pilot, who was more familiar with the operation.

"If you're interested in the course of the *Soucoupe*, you can ask the pilot—or, if you wish, we've rigged a set of mirrors to allow the observer to read the gyrocompass, which is located on the pilot's side." It was hard to convince people that the mirrors really worked, until it was dark enough for them to see the illuminated compass-heading clearly.

"The underwater telephone is back here on the aft end of the water tank. All you have to do is pick up the microphone —push the button—and talk slowly. The phone will be on all the time so that you can hear the surface boat if it calls you."

At this point the observer would usually be sitting up, facing aft, and commenting on the amount of space inside our small craft. He was right—there was a surprising amount of room, even though many things were crowded in—you never got the feeling that you were cramped or overly confined. If there was more time, we would usually go on to point out the pilot controls and some of the other machinery. I would be lying in the pilot's berth. "The controls that the pilot uses are on his left side—here; the two jet controls are moved either together or separately. You can see they go to the two hydraulic actuators and then out to the lines through the hull. Ahead of the two actuators is the rudder control. These three controls keep his left hand busy. Now, he must fully memorize the position, underneath the couch, of the seven or eight buttons and switches on the electrical panel that turn the jets on and off and select fast and slow speeds. Also, several of the light controls are on this board. Farther below he must feel out the mercury control lever, which instantly tilts the *Saucer* bow down or bow up. Even deeper in the recesses is the mechanical arm and claw control which moves in a fore-and-aft direction as well as crosswise for the two different motions —arm in or out and claw open or closed."

Already it sounds as though our pilot might need three hands.

"Finally, there are the two lever controls in between the couches—one drops the 55-pound weights by a simple quick twist and the other lets in small amounts of outside water for ballasting. You can perhaps imagine how busy the pilot is when he is maneuvering the vehicle against a gentle current to pick up an object with the claw—all without seeing any of the controls." After a four-hour dive with much of this kind of activity, each scientist always emerged with a tremendous respect for the pilot and his abilities.

To wind up the tour, I would point out the lever for the emergency weight, mercury jettisoning procedure, the two small aqualungs for breathing in case of fire, an inflatable life raft, and the control for inflating the "jupe"—the conning tower or skirt that could permit emergency escape on the surface in the event of a heavy sea. Few of the many people who made dives in the *Saucer* were really alarmed by mention of emergency procedures and such. Many, of course, were scuba divers, since most marine scientists have learned this skill to aid them in carrying on their investigations underwater. However, quite a few were not completely at home in such a small vehicle—yet none to my knowledge ever panicked or, after seeing the inside, refused to go on a dive. The orderly, organized, and businesslike layout of Captain Cousteau's *Saucer* inspired confidence. Also, the *Diving Saucer* had a spotless record of no accidents or dangerous incidents in a history of over 430 successful dives. Finally, I suppose that knowing something of the basic design and the numerous back-up devices reassured them about its safety.

Then, there were always those who imagined dire situations. "What would you do if the *Saucer* was caught under a ledge with no power?" or, "How do you open the hatch to make a free ascent?" "What if it developed a leak?" A free ascent from any depth more than a few feet is probably impossible and obviously so because there was no way of over-pressuring the *Saucer* to allow the hatch to be opened. Unless the *Saucer* were on the bottom, to bleed in water would not be possible either, since the increased weight would make it sink too rapidly. In giving serious thought to such situations, we always realized that the *Saucer* occupants were as a rule safer if they remained where they were and let those on the surface rig ways of recovery. Happily in our 125 dives not a single occasion arose to involve us in such a recovery.

CHAPTER 4

Men, Methods,

and Missions

The Cargomaster looked like an overgrown pelican—fat and ungainly—its abnormally thick body hovering just off the end of the runway as it was about to land at Los Alamitos Naval Air Station. With a deafening roar the engines reversed pitch and the aircraft gradually slowed down as it approached the taxi strip. A flight that might have taken five or six hours on a passenger airline had taken over three days. There had been several moments when it looked as though the flight would never get to California. The giant airplane had now turned around and was slowly taxiing back toward us and the flat-bed truck ready for our special cargo. It was November 2, 1964.

At this point the local ground crew had waved the plane in and the pilot cut the four engines. Although they weren't much bigger than those on commercial craft, these engines and the whole plane seemed considerably larger because of the great girth of the body and the height of the flight deck. Presently, with a whining and mysterious clanking, the front loading ramp and swing-up nose of the Cargomaster opened to show an even more unbelievable, warehouse-like interior. At the same time the three Frenchmen climbed down a ladder amidships. They greeted Joe Thompson and Larry Somers with great warmth as long-lost friends. Finally we spotted Jerry Burnett, smiling but weary. We were all introduced to each man of the French group from OFRS, with whom we would be working closely over the next months.

André Laban had come for several weeks to assist us in the operation of the *Saucer*, especially that involving our launch techniques and the equipping of the *Saucer* for the scientists. He represented Captain Cousteau, who wished to make sure that everything would go smoothly in our joint venture. André was 36 years old, the Technical Director of OFRS, and a most accomplished underwater expert. He spoke English well, understood it even better, and had been to this country several times. He wore an Air Force-type blue jacket with a fur collar, which always served as his traveling coat on later occasions. He has a striking appearance when one first meets him, for his head is closely shaven in the manner of some Europeans.

Our Chief Maintenance Technician, Jacques Roux, was wearing black coveralls. He had come to California on the first *Saucer* project and was pleased to be back. He was better known to all as "Gaston"—his French nickname. Gaston had spoken very little English before his first trip, but after working with Americans that one month he had picked up a lot. Now, although he spoke it slowly he understood it well and improved immensely as we went along. He was responsible for the mechanical and electrical performance of the *Saucer*. He had been with it since its conception in 1956 and probably knew as much about it as anyone. As maintenance technician, he took fond care of the *Soucoupe* and was at first admittedly guarding it from some of our seemingly "wild" schemes for scientific diving. Gaston was 32, short and slight, with a large black moustache and a quick smile.

Finally, the third of the group was Raymond Kientzy, an ex-combat diver from the French Navy, who had been with Cousteau since 1952. He was widely experienced in working at sea and was to be the pilot of the *Saucer*. It was his first trip to the United States and he spoke little English. Like Jacques Roux of the Cousteau team, Raymond also had a nickname. Since he had had a small canoe as a child that he had paddled everywhere, the name stuck—"Canoe," pronounced "Cano-e."

The formalities over, we all pitched in to help unload the supplies, tools, spare-parts boxes, duffle bags, iron weights, batteries, and other items for the *Saucer*. Since our contract for the *Saucer* involved the U.S. Navy and the point of departure in France was remote, it turned out to be less expensive for the government to use the Military Air Transport Service (MATS).

We walked around to the front of the plane. The ramp that would allow the *Saucer* to be rolled out was firmly planted. Jerry and Gaston began to direct the unloading. We could see in the dark recesses of the plane the familiar yellow, oval-shaped vehicle, looking small and lost in its hangar. While the plane's crew rigged lines, our team had finished loading boxes onto the 65-foot flatbed trailer. It seemed that we had rented a very large truck to handle such a small load; our gear, including the 4-ton *Saucer,* was not to take up more than 15 feet of the enormous trailer. I'm sure the French thought this typically American extravagance—or, more likely, thought it perfectly normal.

We were now ready for the main unloading. Joe positioned himself strategically to get good coverage with the 16mm movie camera; since he was our official photographer it was his job to get all the documentary footage. He intended to film enough to make a 30-minute documentary movie of our whole operation. Slowly the *Saucer* began to emerge from the

Cargomaster, inching its way down the two-track ramp on its own wheeled dolly. The Air Force crew paid out gradually on a block and a tackle while Gaston guided the front wheels. Joe began the movie sequence. Gaston squinted, frowned, then shook his head in disapproval.

"Is wrong," he said loudly, holding up his hand like a gendarme in Paris. "Back—again."

Gaston's few words, along with the gesticulations, got the meaning across immediately.

"Oh, Gaston, why do you stop now? It was a perfect scene," said Joe lamenting the half-finished sequence of the *Saucer's* entry onto American soil.

Gaston explained briefly that the rails weren't adjusted parallel and that in moving the *Saucer* farther down one of the wheels might have slipped off. So back into the hangar went *La Soucoupe* after a false start. With a degree of perfection we would all become aware of later—and be very grateful for—Gaston carefully aligned the rails and took sights on the dolly wheels, as the *Saucer* stood at the edge of the stage poised and ready for its next entrance.

"Necessary adjust," said Gaston, and pointed to the right. The rail was moved a fraction of an inch. He knelt, squinted again, and said finally, "OK."

The show began again. Joe shot footage, the *Saucer* rolled smoothly this time, and everyone was happy. From here the *Saucer* was picked up by a long-boomed "cherry picker," placed gently on the long flatbed truck, and chained down securely. The first leg of the trip and subsequent operation of the *Diving Saucer* began as we drove along the boulevards behind the truck, with the strange yellow object perched atop it looking like a weird creature with huge round eyes.

I listened to the tales of the flight over the Atlantic and all the problems that had arisen. The C-124C had flown into Marseille on schedule and taken the *Saucer* aboard easily. Jerry and the three Frenchmen settled down in the noisy plane as best they could, sharing the quarters with the crew. Shortly after they had left France they realized that their progress was extremely slow, due to strong head winds. A C-

124C is not fast to begin with; in head winds it is really slow.

The first stop was at the Azores. Here the crew took their required break and the remainder of the first day was lost. The large plane had barely climbed to its cruising altitude when someone discovered trouble in the cargo area. Riding along in the plane were several caskets coming back to the States—full.

The wide-eyed crewman rushed forward to the cockpit and told Jerry, "One of the caskets is beginning to move and the top's about to come open!"

There was a simple explanation. In the unpressurized cabin of the flight deck the caskets had to have a pressure relief valve at high altitude. A quick check showed that this one was not functioning. Rather than risk an explosion, the pilot decided to turn back. The only trouble was that the C-124C had fueled for the long trip to the United States. To land now it had to dump gasoline. This process took several hours of circling. Finally the plane landed.

By the time the repair was made there wasn't time to get in another flying day, so the plane, crew, and *Saucer* stayed over. On routine flights the crew usually flies 15 hours and then sleeps. Everyone who has ridden one of these air freighters always mentions the high noise level that can become very fatiguing. Some crewmen wear ear plugs—others hear the airplane engines for days after.

On the third day the C-124C landed in Newark, Delaware, their first point in the United States. The customs routine and immigration were handled easily. The three Frenchmen and Jerry went to have a bite to eat. When they returned the *Saucer* was nowhere to be seen.

"*Mon Dieu!*" exclaimed Gaston and André together, "*La Soucoupe* is gone."

After a frantic search, they discovered the cargo and the *Saucer* safe and unharmed in a storage area. The off-duty crew had decided to unload and in the brief time they took for coffee had done so and left. So Jerry had to convince the new crew that everything had to be reloaded. This episode thoroughly unnerved Gaston and he wouldn't part with the

Soucoupe again. André was not alarmed. Canoe, I'm sure, thought all Americans were crazy.

It was, then, the morning of the fourth day when our tired and worn gang arrived in California. By the time we got to Long Beach it must have seemed a long haul from France. Everything went smoothly and Fred Willett had the *Hugh Tide* all prepared for the *Saucer*.

We off-loaded the *Saucer,* using the 22-ton hydraulic crane on the ship. Fred operated it to swing the *Saucer* off the truck. I had the dubious honor of being the passenger perched precariously on the side of the *Saucer,* holding tightly to the bridle while we rocked to and fro. The control of the crane was precise and quick—for a moment I was out over the water, then around down on the deck of the ship. The *Saucer,* with the cradle dolly, but without the wheels, was then welded to the deck. The spot selected was as close as possible to the crane, to give us more work space.

When I had first seen the *Hugh Tide,* I thought its deck was fairly roomy. It had a forward deckhouse extending to midship. Abaft this was a cargo hatch and open deck. Now, with one of our 8 × 8 vans on port side, the crane taking up at least 12 × 15 feet, the *Saucer,* 10 feet in diameter, in the center of the deck, and finally a 17-foot Boston whaler, we were crowded, to say the least. The *Hugh Tide* had been designed as a work boat, but with some specific requirements for oceanographic research work. She was deep and rode well in a sea. There was ample crew space. She was not perfectly suited to our operation—we needed much more deck space —but she would get us through the month until the larger *Burch Tide* would arrive from the Gulf of Mexico.

Many of our original plans couldn't be carried out, owing to the space limitations on *Hugh Tide.* The one 8 × 8 van had to serve as the photographic darkroom and camera storeroom, and the electronic and mechanical workshops. This was quite a lot of activity for one 8-foot cube. There were times later when we felt we were staging the original telephone-booth feat. The van was furnished with an 8-foot workbench on one side, with drawers underneath. For the other wall we had specified shelves, floor to ceiling, leaving space in the far corner for a small refrigerator to keep our film supply cool. The entrance was large and had two doors measuring 5 feet across. These were hardly ideal for the darkroom, but it was the best we could do in the time available. Much of the support equipment and consumables, including six or eight large gray metal boxes with all the *Saucer* spares, were consigned to the hold. The *Hugh Tide* had cargo space below reached through a large deck hatch. All cargo that wasn't safe on deck, such as battery chargers, spare batteries, scuba gear, etc., was stashed in this area and in the after-sleeping quarters. Since the bridge was small and filled with navigation instruments, we had to put our echo sounder in the aft cabin below. Normally on such a ship there would be a deck laboratory for these and other survey instruments, but our need for all available open deck space wouldn't allow it.

With everything loaded, the *Hugh Tide* looked like a kind of large, unwieldy, and slightly top-heavy circus. However, before we could be certified by maritime law we had to pass a stability tipping test. The crane installation was inspected by an underwriter from the insurance company, then Fred had to demonstrate that it could pick up a heavy load without excessively heeling the ship. A heavy cylindrical buoy that had been used in the same proof test in February on the earlier operation still lay on the pier. It reportedly weighed some 22,000 pounds. The crane neatly reached up to the dock, hooked onto this buoy, and proceeded to dunk it from various positions out to 34 feet over the stern and the quarter. Each time the ship heeled, but not enough to concern the marine surveyor. Finally it was decided that the installation was safe and that the heavy crane was not going to endanger the stability of the ship.

Much of the support equipment for the operation that could not be placed aboard the *Hugh Tide* we left behind on the pier at Long Beach for our return the following month, when the *Burch Tide* would be available. These included the air compressor for diving tanks, spare tanks, and diving consumables such as extra weights and oil.

Luckily, the first month's schedule did not require long-distance steaming or difficult operating sites. We felt as though we would have some chance to learn operating techniques before the going got rougher.

With a shrill toot on the ship's horn, one of the deck hands flipped off the remaining spring line from the piling, and the *Hugh Tide* smartly maneuvered away from the dock in mid-afternoon, bound for San Diego, some 100 miles to the south. Three of us stood on shore watching the strange-looking ship with bright orange crane and yellow *Saucer* move slowly down the long finger pier to the main channel. We had declined the offer of riding the next ten hours aboard, since all our work had been done. We felt it was time for us to spend a little while with our families, whom we had neglected the last week or longer. We took the easy way out and drove to San Diego. It was just as well too, for we certainly would get our fill of riding about on boats over the next several months.

The following morning the ship arrived at "B" Street pier in San Diego. We were going to occupy the corner of the pier next to FLIP (Floating Instrument Platform), the unique and specially designed device for Scripps. This spar-like vessel that looks like an enormous pencil is 354 feet long and takes up the entire end of the pier. It measures about 15 feet in diameter. The upper section, made up of crew quarters and engine room, is 50 feet long and about 30 feet across. This part remains above water when FLIP turns to a vertical position. The rest is submerged, giving the craft great stability. This feature of stability made FLIP valuable as a measuring platform in rough seas, since there was almost no roll and never more than a foot or two of vertical motion. Further, it was an excellent listening platform since there was almost no ship noise.

By mid-morning the *Hugh Tide*, and especially the area around the *Saucer*, was swarming with scientists, technicians, reporters, and bystanders who had gotten word of our arrival in San Diego. Two or three technicians from the Naval Electronics Laboratory were busy fitting on the temperature sensor, current meter, and the communications equipment that all the scientists would share. The French were helping, but at times you could see that they were upset by the number of persons all climbing in and out of the *Saucer*. It was the mass-production approach. One of the modifications that had to be made was the installation of an extra penetrator, a through-hull fitting that brings electrical leads though the hull from the outside. A penetrator was a precisely made fitting that allowed wiring to pass through but kept water out. This additional penetrator came through the hull where one of the three small hemispherical ports normally was. The port had a double sealing arrangement which insured that even if the outside part were smashed, no water could enter it. Our new penetrator was needed in order to get enough additional electrical leads to run the special devices that were being added. The addition of these wires brought the total to 26 single wires. The installation was one that the pilots watched carefully, since their lives depended on watertight integrity where any through-hull penetrations were involved.

Early in the afternoon several of the scientists from Scripps and NEL came aboard to view the progress and to begin to outline the program ahead of us. Dr. E. L. (Jerry) Winterer, a smiling, cheerful, sandy-haired young man, represented Scripps. He was an experienced geologist who had newly come, as it were, from the dry land to the sea. He hoped to learn more about the contemporaneous processes that go on in the sea and to relate these to the geology of the California coast and structures. Dr. Winterer was to be our coordinator at Scripps in arranging the diving schedules for nearly a dozen of their scientists. He would also make a number of dives himself. Since Scripps was the principal contractor, Dr. Winterer agreed also to coordinate the other five Navy agencies that had contracted for our services.

NEL was represented by Dr. Robert F. Dill, a marine geologist who had been working with research submersibles for nearly ten years. Almost half the number of the proposed dives with the *Saucer* were going to be made for NEL scientists, so he was on hand to help in the planning of the first month's operations. Dr. Dill had made some early dives in the

Diving Saucer and *Trieste I* before either vehicle had come to the United States. He was one of the pioneers of submersible programs at NEL and had been instrumental in securing support for the Diving Saucer program.

Dr. Winterer began to outline the proposed schedule of dives, planning hopefully to use every day but Sunday. We were to start in the San Diego area near Scripps Canyon during the first two weeks, to let us shake down the operation. Then our floating home would move 60 miles northward up the coast for a short series of dives, including a few around the outer islands toward San Nicolas, finally winding up in Long Beach near the end of November. At that point we expected to have the *Burch Tide* ready and transfer to it. We checked over the names of the scientists and the particular type of dives each might wish to make. Dr Winterer had decided to undertake the first dive in Scripps Canyon. Although this narrow canyon had been well explored by the previous *Saucer* expedition, there was interest in making observations at a different time of year to see if there might be appreciable seasonal effects on the amount of sediment or its transport as well as changes in canyon features. There had been considerable speculation about the possible strengths and speeds of water currents through this canyon, as well as other canyons like it, and more information was needed. One of the scientists especially concerned was Dr. Douglas Inman of Scripps, who had established a reputation in sediments and beach processes. He had been conducting a program of current measurements in the head of Scripps Canyon using divers and, at greater depths, moored instruments. The dive for Dr. Inman was to be followed by one for Dr. Shepard, then one for Dr. Dill. Thus, the first series was entirely geological in nature and required no special equipment other than that normally aboard the *Saucer*.

CHAPTER 5

Scripps Canyon

We were underway shortly after our planned 0800 departure from the "B" Street mooring the next day on our way to Scripps Pier. We steamed out of San Diego harbor, along the narrow point of land with steep banks to the north that is occupied by the Navy Submarine Base, NEL, and many of the large World War II bunkers and fortifications. The sea around Point Loma was calm—a wonderful introduction for me to the Pacific Ocean—with a barely perceptible long swell and no wind ripples. The weather had been unusually warm for several days. Although we knew we could work in rougher water, it was a blessing to have such perfect weather in which to start since most of the Westinghouse crew were new. The *Hugh Tide* plodded steadily at 9 knots a mile or two offshore, passing Mission Beach, Pacific Beach, and finally coming to La Jolla by late morning. Scripps Pier extends 1,500 feet into the sea off the steep cliffs. The ship lay to a half mile off the pier and waited for the scientific party to join us by boat from the pier. As soon as the ship had stopped we had started the crane, picked up the small boat, and put it over the side. Jerry Burnett manned it. He was familiar with our launching techniques and knew how to maneuver the small boat for recovery of the *Saucer*.

While preparation of the *Saucer* went on under the direction of Gaston, Canoe discussed the objective of the dive with Dr. Jerry Winterer. Fortunately, Jerry Winterer spoke French fluently so the pre-dive briefing went smoothly. We had decided that it was desirable for the scientist to outline the objectives of his dive with the pilot. At this time he would show on a chart where he wished to go, where he might like to sample or observe, whether he wanted photographs or samples, and how far he wanted to go.

Dr. Winterer unrolled a large chart that showed Scripps Canyon, the pier, and depth contours. He pointed to the approximate location on the chart of the taut wire buoy that we could see not far from the ship. He explained to Canoe that he wished to descend close to this buoy, on whose wire a current meter would be sent down by divers. Part of his objective was to observe the meter location and see if it was in a proper place to measure currents in the canyon—if they even existed. If the buoy anchor location was not in a good place for measuring the current, *Hugh Tide* would move the buoy to a better spot. This last, of course, necessitated the use of the underwater "telephone" for communication. Following this, Dr. Winterer wanted to traverse a slope on the rim of the canyon and see if there were any signs of slope sediment being transported into the axis of the submarine canyon below. Such evidence would be of special interest to geologists.

Shortly before one in the afternoon André Laban got word from Gaston and Canoe that all was ready. Several very careful checks had been made to see that nothing had gone awry with the *Saucer* in the trans-Atlantic flight. I watched Canoe walk around the *Saucer* looking casually at everything just before the fiberglas covers were put on. Actually it was a careful inspection, although the pilots always manage to appear casual. Canoe performed his "walk around" with the aplomb of a pioneer airplane pilot who made the rounds of his craft before departure, occasionally poking, pulling, or inspecting. It was time to dive. Jerry Winterer climbed into the sphere. Canoe sprang nimbly up the ladder, then paused part way in the hatch to check the fit of the "O" ring in the hatch cover. It was extremely important that this rubber gasket should fit in its groove and that there were no nicks or cuts. Like any container designed to keep water out, the gasket and the seal it makes are most vulnerable right at the surface, before the pressure makes the seal tight. Next Canoe disappeared into the *Saucer*, pulling the hatch closed. The handle spun around several times, tightening the hatch dogs. Conversation ensued over the hardwire telephone plugged into the vehicle linking Gaston and Canoe. Everything was OK.

Joe Thompson was operating the crane for his first launch. He concentrated on Fred Willett, who was giving the lifting signs. With only the 4 tons of the *Saucer* on it, the crane was extremely sensitive to operate. If the control wasn't handled gently the *Saucer* would be jerked up. Joe slowly eased the *Saucer* about a foot and a half up off its cradle. The crane and *Saucer*, followed by Gaston walking with the telephone, began to move slowly to the right. Fred with the CB radio, and two of us with steadying lines, moved around the stern until the *Saucer* hung out over the water. As I held onto one of the lines I could see Jerry Winterer peering through the porthole smiling, ready to venture into a world few people had ever seen. Larry Somers had put on a small scuba "rescuepak"; since he was hook-up diver for the day he might have to be underwater briefly. Everything appeared nearly perfect. The ship was just where it should be.

The dive was to start with the *Saucer* descending a tautwire buoy line to a known spot on the bottom. The *Saucer* is attached to the taut-wire line by a shackle that can slide along the wire. The mechanical arm-claw holds the shackle. At the bottom the pilot simply releases the claw's grip on the shackle.

This technique permits the *Saucer* to land at a particular site even if there is a current, thus avoiding unnecessary hunting and waste of valuable dive time.

At 1305 Fred Willett gave Joe the down sign for the crane and the *Saucer* was lowered toward the water still attached on the automatic hook. Just as the bottom of the *Saucer* touched the surface Fred gave a tug on the trip line and the hook jaw released, letting the *Saucer* slip into the water. On that first launch I was holding the tag line, which at this moment was the only thing supporting the *Saucer*. Usually the weight of the 4-ton submersible in water at launch is about 50 pounds. It seemed more like 100 this time—but I really had nothing to judge by and I hung on. While the tag line was connected and the diver was removing the lifting bridle, the pilot had a chance to inspect the hatch for leaks and to check other systems, such as propulsion, mercury trim, lights, and other controls. He then talked over the telephone to the deck control to say he was ready. The check was thorough on this first dive.

In the meantime, Larry was unfastening three large shackles on the bridle and swimming with it to the small boat where Jerry Burnett and Tom Horton were attending. Everyone was slow and nearly five minutes had gone by; the *Hugh Tide* had drifted about 100 yards away from the target area and the taut-wire buoy. Once a launch was started and the vehicle was in the water we would not use the main power of the ship, for the propellers could endanger the diver and the *Saucer*. The small boat was standing close by and André, who had been carefully watching our procedure—especially the new hook—suggested that the *Saucer* be towed to the location. The *Saucer* didn't tow well, but it could be pulled very slowly by the small boat. The towline was snapped on to two rings on the front of the *Saucer*. As the strain was taken by the boat we cast off the supporting tag line. Larry followed along, ready to put the *Saucer* on the buoy line. Unfortunately, since the *Saucer* was trimmed much too heavily, it planed down deep as the boat pulled it. Soon we realized that they weren't getting anywhere, so André signaled Jerry and

Tom to stop and pull the *Saucer* up to release it. The small boat was now drifting farther away. At first Jerry thought that André wanted them to cast off the towline. Larry had descended to the *Saucer*. As Jerry and Tom held the line, which had a great deal of strain, André was making great motions and shouting, "Pull! Pull!"

Below, Larry was frantically trying to unsnap the hooks, but the strain on the line prevented this. As he pulled for a bit of slack from the surface, the small-boat tenders were pulling on the line in the opposite direction. He was now at a depth of 60 feet and it was lucky he had thought to wear the small "rescue-pak" breathing apparatus, which was a miniature scuba tank with ten minutes' supply of air. Finally Larry managed to get enough slack to release the hooks, although by this time he was ready to cut them off. The *Saucer* descended toward the bottom to begin Dive 231.

As we collected ourselves after our first launch André pointed out why he had been so concerned. Had the small-boat crew cast off the 75-foot towline still attached to the *Saucer* it could have easily become fouled on many objects in the canyon and possibly have trapped the *Saucer* at a depth beyond diver rescue. We realized that we had to plan our dives thoroughly and be ready for occurrences that required quick and correct decisions.

In the *Saucer*, Canoe had been aware that the launch routine was slow, but he was not sure what was causing the delay until he saw Larry tugging at the towing bridle hooks in an attempt to release them. Finally, when the lines had slackened, they were unsnapped and the *Saucer* began its descent. It was already at about 20 meters. The water was slightly murky, but not what would be called dirty. Canoe sat up momentarily and glanced over at the echo sounder, which showed the bottom as a slanting line. This slanting line really indicated the rate of descent as the *Saucer* closed the distance to the bottom. When they were about 10 to 15 meters from the bottom, he released the descent weight and the *Saucer* slowed its descent.

Jerry Winterer pressed up close to the port and presently

could see the silty bottom. He estimated the visibility at several meters and Canoe agreed. The depth gauge read close to 50 meters. All was well. Now where exactly was the anchor of the taut-wire buoy and in what direction should they proceed? Jerry Winterer had suggested we use an instrument that had worked with success on the *Saucer* in February. It was a type of receiver that could determine the direction of pinger-sound source and thereby help in steering the vehicle to a particular spot. The receiver used a dish antenna on the outside of the *Saucer* that would receive the 37-kilocycle pinger signal and a small amplifier inside that the pilot or observer could hear. The small boat used exactly the same receiver to track the *Saucer* from the surface.

The receiver crackled with occasional static, but there was no anticipated "chirp-chirp" from the pinger. Could the *Saucer* have drifted too far away in the short descent time? It didn't seem possible. Jerry Winterer decided he would at least report that they were on the bottom and perhaps the tracking boat could recommend a course to the buoy. He pushed the microphone button and spoke into it.

"This is the *Soucoupe*. . . . We are at the bottom at 50 meters. The visibility is 3 to 4 meters and murky. The temperature sensor says 25 degrees Centigrade and the current meter is barely moving. What course to the buoy? Can you hear us?"

Silence. They waited. He transmitted again—this time only trying to establish contact. Silence. Perhaps the underwater telephone wasn't transmitting or perhaps no one was listening. It certainly was a silent world—even at these relatively shallow depths. Canoe said that they should move on, so he switched the propulsion motor to full speed and trimmed the buoyancy slightly to bring the *Saucer* off the bottom. A cloud of fine sediment was stirred up as they moved off in a direction that Canoe felt by "the seat of his pants" was right. Pilots of all vehicles have this built-in, innate sense that prevails where many sophisticated navigational devices fail.

Jerry noted that the bottom was a gently sloping 10 to 15 degrees, if he judged correctly, and composed of a fairly fine-grained silt and muddy sediment. What he really wanted to find out was how this fine material was transported into the deep and narrow submarine canyon some 2 kilometers away. The scientists at Scripps had determined earlier that the canyon was a large conduit for sediments—both coarser sands beginning at the canyon head and these finer silts along the way. Sampling in much deeper water out in the San Diego trough showed a mixture of both coarse and fine.

During the time the *Saucer* was moving along, its occupants listened for the pinger, but with no success. They suspected that there was too much interference in the various electrical systems of the *Saucer*. Canoe stopped the pump motor that drove the water jets—they drifted quietly for a while. Still no sound. Then suddenly a large object loomed ahead. It appeared gigantic to Jerry. Canoe switched on the bright headlights. There ahead lay the lead weights of the buoy anchor. At first it had looked nearly the size of a man, but as they approached it turned out to be only several feet high. Jerry remembered that things invariably appear larger than their size seen underwater. The anchor was at most 30 inches high. There beside it was the red and green pinger lying in complete silence . . . or maybe it was cheerfully pinging away, but the saucernauts couldn't hear it. It had done them little good.

Canoe set the *Saucer* down near the anchor and they inspected the area within view as a suitable location for measuring currents. Jerry could see no large rocks or mounds that would obstruct or change a current reading. The site was fine. Now to tell the divers to send the Savonious current meter down the wire. He tried the telephone again, asking for acknowledgment. He paused, waited, but still there was no reply. Canoe commented that he really hadn't expected the telephone to work and that in France they didn't use one anyway. But to their surprise, as they watched, the yellow current meter came sliding into view, landing safely about 4 feet off the bottom. So they could communicate, even if only in one direction. The meter began to turn slowly. Jerry switched on the current meter in the *Saucer* and the needle moved up to about .2 of a knot at times. This was really more than he had expected, but it was still very slow. Canoe moved the *Saucer* slowly into a better position so Jerry could get some pictures of the current meter as it functioned. Then Canoe switched on the bright movie light and took some footage of the meter, while Jerry took some still pictures with the 35mm camera.

This completed, they started the second part of the mission, a traverse along the canyon rim. Canoe started the *Saucer* on a westerly course as they passed over a sloping mud bottom. Everywhere they looked there was activity. Flatfish, almost completely buried, when disturbed would surprisedly undulate away, moving a small bit of sediment down slope. Worms, octopus, and other fish all dwelled in or on the bottom and made their living at turning over the bottom. On the slopes, which were increasing from 15 to 25 degrees, this kind of activity could be significant in producing a slow, gradual downward creep of the sediment. There were also bits of marine vegetation that looked as though they had moved down slope. There were balls and wads of eel grass and pieces of kelp. The whole picture seemed to indicate a motion. Occasionally Jerry asked Canoe to stop the *Soucoupe*. They would rest it on the bottom, then watch the movement of bits of flotsam. Currents indicated were as high as ¼ of a knot.

They started again on their way, still heading on course 270 degrees, using the gyrocompass to steer by. As the slope increased so, of course, did the depth. The gauge read about 75 meters when they reached a rather abrupt change in environment. As the slope was nearly 30 degrees they came to a precipitous cliff which represented the border between the silty-muddy area and a rocky outcrop area that dropped off steeply over the rim of the canyon. It was another world, Jerry remarked, due to this sharp delineation. Around the rocks there were forms of coral, among them the familiar gorgonian corals associated with rocky areas. Fish of all sorts swam amongst the rocks. The saucernauts noticed that in the water over the canyon the visibility improved markedly, increasing to nearly 10 meters. They moved along slowly, following the border line for some time and taking still photographs. At one point Jerry saw a very bright object, quite large, shining in the distance. Excitedly he told Canoe to go toward it. When they reached it, much to Jerry's disappointment and chagrin, it was a beer can.

Farther along they came on a good example of a slump, a place where a large portion of sediment slope had broken away and slid down. Slumps arc usually identified by a fresh scar. This feature was one that some of the scientists believed to be quite prevalent on steep banks, indicating a mass movement of the sediment. As they moved in to photograph and examine the scar, Jerry could see that it was recent and deep enough to expose the non-oxidized area of a greenish color. It measured 2 feet across by about 10 feet in length and was close to a rock outcrop. This was the only such scar feature the saucernauts had seen on their dive.

As they took the last photograph of the scar, Canoe noticed that the strobe light had not flashed. He asked Jerry to try again. No flash. It was likely that after three hours of use the camera batteries were too low to charge the condenser for the unit. Perhaps they had not been put on charge soon enough the evening before. Canoe decided it would be wise to return to the surface, since there were no communications and several of the other instruments weren't working; also, there was a new surface crew. There would be time for more dives here. Jerry agreed that they had gone far enough to see a good sample of the bottom and to know that it was representative of a large area. Canoe reached over and turned the handle that dropped the second 55-pound weight. The *Saucer* slowly departed from the bottom. Canoe picked up the microphone, still doubting that it really worked, and said, "Here is *Soucoupe* . . . on way to surface."

From 85 meters it takes less than five minutes to reach the surface. The *Saucer* then lies there, waiting for the retrieval process. As is customary in the French operations, the saucernauts radio that they are on the surface, so that the small tending boat can be alerted. As a visual marker, the pilot of the *Saucer* turns the water jets up and shoots a stream of water 15 to 20 feet in the air.

Canoe first turned on the newly installed citizens band radio and started to call the *Hugh Tide*. There was no answer. He called again. Still none. So he turned the jets up and shot a stream of water.

By this time Larry and Jerry Burnett had already seen the *Saucer* and they moved in to attach the lifting bridle. All three vehicles—the ship, the small boat, and the *Saucer*—had CB radios. So while the ship and the boat communicated they couldn't talk to the *Saucer*. This didn't hinder the operation, however, and the *Hugh Tide* took position some 30 to 40 feet from the *Saucer* and laid to with stern toward it. Larry had finished putting on the bridle and was leading the tag to the *Saucer* and back when we, who were standing on the stern of the ship, realized that the line was twisted. The operation had to be repeated, making several more trips for Larry to swim. As I found out later, when it was my turn to perform this task, this was an easy and common mistake to make, but after a bit of swimming back and forth I didn't make it again.

The sea was still calm with a long low swell. The deck crew hauled on the line and while the small boat pulled gently the opposite way, to keep the *Saucer* from coming in too close to the ship, we got it positioned for the automatic hookup. The large bridle ring slipped neatly into the hook jaw and Fred pulled the line that should shut it. But Murphy's Law or its correlative, the Law of Maximum Perversity, seemed to be in effect—things don't seem to work properly the first time. The jaw would not close. We pulled, and Fred pulled, and finally André said we should close it by hand. Larry carefully swam in over the *Saucer* and, avoiding the crane boom, brought the bottom latch of the hook closed with a solid click. Joe eased up on the crane and the *Saucer*, with its two occupants smiling out the ports, was lifted clear of the water, swung around, and lowered onto the cradle.

Our cook, Little Joe, met the saucernauts with two cups of hot cocoa, an offering that from this time onwards became customary after dives.

Thus ended our first dive. The mission had been accomplished, even though a number of pieces of equipment had not functioned properly. Jerry Winterer was pleased with his observations. I discussed the dive with him in a debriefing session, using a tape recorder. He and the rest of his scientific party departed for the Scripps pier nearby, as the *Hugh Tide* started for San Diego.

Fred called us to the wardroom, where we had a critique on the dive. We discussed the launching episode and the need for better handling techniques. Aboard the *Saucer*, the pinger receiver, underwater telephone, temperature sensor, and radio had all failed to operate. Such were the problems of underwater instruments. We knew these problems could be solved. Jerry Burnett and Gaston were already at work in the *Soucoupe*.

The ship reached the San Diego pier at 7:30 that evening. Repair work began as NEL technicians came aboard to help fix instruments they had installed. It was late when I reached my apartment in La Jolla.

The following three or four days diving with the geologists in and around Scripps and La Jolla Canyons saw improvement as we smoothed out our operation.

By Sunday we felt we were old hands and decided that since we were on schedule with our Scripps divers we would take a saucernaut's holiday and give our two pilot trainees some experience. At the same time, since we had all been almost unseen at home, we invited our families to join us on the *Hugh Tide* for an outing. With everyone aboard just after noon, we headed for a spot off Point Loma near the harbor of San Diego.

For the occasion, Little Joe prepared his delicious doughnuts. These were especially appealing to the French. Whenever he smelled the doughnuts frying Gaston would open his eyes wide and exclaim, "O rings!" Thereafter, doughnuts were exclusively called "O rings," after the circular rubber sealing gaskets of the same shape.

André took over as instructor for Joe and Larry. Since the dives were made in 30 to 50 meters a few miles offshore we saw no reason to track the *Saucer*. Most of us sat or lay on deck relaxing. It was our first chance to be together since we had left the East Coast.

Joe and Larry returned from their hour-long dives with great respect for the *Saucer* and all that its operation entailed. They conceded that a good deal of experience was required before the controls could be found and operated in the dark. A very slight bit of rudder or a single jet would spin the *Saucer* right around, overcontrolling it. The rest of us were envious and hoped to get a chance just to make a dive. Fred wanted to give the maximum time to the trainees and then, in what time remained, let each of the others have one dive.

We continued diving for Scripps marine geologists as they inspected parts of Scripps and La Jolla Canyons. All of these men, Drs. Shepard, Dill, and Inman, had made dives in the first *Saucer* series and were now able to make valuable deductions from dives at different seasons. They were interested in finding examples of sediment behavior and transport into the canyons and through the canyons into much deeper water.

The purpose of their study was to determine by direct observation how great volumes of sand and silt were moved from the shore to points several miles offshore. Dr. Shepard concluded from his dives that filling of the canyons by sediment had certainly been the most important change since his dive last winter. He noted pulsating currents in Scripps Canyon of, at times, half a knot. Dr. Dill observed the same type of current in La Jolla Canyon where it joins Scripps Canyon nearly a mile offshore. As a rule these currents didn't interfere with the *Saucer* operation, but on one dive in Scripps Canyon Dr. Inman and André bounced around on one wall and had to ascend to get away from the turbulent effect. During the debriefing Dr. Inman mentioned as an interesting observation that he had counted as many as 10 wire cables over a distance of 30 feet running over a rocky point and disappearing down deeper into the canyon. Some were old and encrusted, others new. Although this fact didn't seem significant at the time, it was of great concern on a later dive in this same area.

The canyon environment was of extreme interest to the geologists, but it made diving difficult, since it was narrow, rocky, and had variable currents and obstructions. Early in the operation it became clear to me why a small submersible like Cousteau's was so valuable to the scientist and why larger ones—especially of the bathyscaphe size—were useless for exploring and investigating such narrow passages.

We had seen that weather could easily limit our efforts and had to cancel several dives because of rough water, heavy swell, or poor visibility. We hoped that when we transferred the operation to our larger ship we could work in rougher seas more safely.

After a few dives off the more open slopes in the San Diego area we were to start a new series on schedule. We were now beginning our third week of diving. We had become experienced enough to strike off for the islands lying offshore—Santa Catalina, San Clemente, and San Nicolas.

Our base of operation shifted from the public pier at "B" Street to the Navy Electronics Laboratory facilities on Point Loma. Our commuting distance to work was slightly shorter, and now that we were in a Navy-controlled area we had to wear badges and attach stickers to our vehicles. All of us used scooters or motor bikes, except Val.

Our little group arrived at the NEL pier, each with duffel as if for a long sea voyage. We would be gone for a week at the islands and then to Long Beach to change ships, followed by two weeks of diving at San Clemente Island.

The *Hugh Tide* loaded supplies and people and steamed off with a compliment of 21—a full house. Our quarters were adequate but not luxurious. The ship had been designed for oceanographic work, with sleeping quarters below, except those for the Master and Chief Scientist, which were on deck. The rest of us, 19, were in two areas—one with tiers of bunks, freezers, and all our diving gear next to the engine room. Forward of this was a larger area for about ten persons. We were crowded, but since it was only for a week it would be bearable. The ship was round-bottomed and had an easy motion. Sleep came quickly.

The objective of the dives was twofold. Two biologists from the Naval Missile Center (NMC) at Point Mugu wanted to inspect Farnsworth Bank near Santa Catalina for a possible site to set up a permanent underwater observation station. Two men from the Pacific Missile Range (PMR) wanted to experiment with tracking bottom-mounted pingers.

Farnsworth Bank lies several miles off Santa Catalina on a fairly smooth sandy shelf about 80 meters deep. The bank is a slender pinnacle that rises to within 8 meters of the surface. Jim Moldenhauer of NMC was the observer and Canoe the pilot. André had left us briefly to return to OFRS and see how things were progressing in France.

We assembled on deck for our dive at Farnsworth Bank. By this time all members of the Westinghouse crew were wearing a gray uniform with a patch that said *Deepstar*. But our French counterparts were far more dashing in their black coveralls. Canoe usually wore a green stretch suit that resembled ski wear. Under this, he wore a white or gray turtleneck sweater and if it was cold he put his black coveralls over all this. Although all French divers and underwater workers are noted for their elf-like red knitted caps, Canoe never wore one. He always had a pipe in his mouth—sometimes it was the thin-stemmed white clay pipe or more likely the larger crooknecked Sherlock Holmes version. His outfit was completed by a kind of chukka boot of very soft leather with a crepe sole. Both he and André wore these boots. In this ensemble, Canoe would stroll about on deck with his hands clasped behind him watching the preparations—a contented smile on his face—until at the appointed moment he would climb lightly to the hatch and disappear inside.

The *Saucer* was launched on a bright clear morning in a nearly flat sea. Four divers were in the water: two NMC Navy divers and Joe and Larry for the purpose of taking photographs of the *Saucer* descending. The water was exceptionally clear and the divers reported that they could see the top of the bank about 50 feet below. They followed the *Saucer* down as it descended at about 60 feet per minute along the almost vertical wall of the bank. At about 125 feet they ran out of film and decided to surface. The *Saucer* continued to 250 feet. Joe returned to the surface and excitedly described the bank as being covered with luxuriant growth and abounding with fish. I spent the dive riding comfortably in the tracking boat, drifting slowly, occasionally starting the engine to move back so that we were directly over the *Saucer*. Since the dive was wholly in the proximity of the bank we had an easy time. Our underwater telephone functioned better than it had in the beginning, but it still was far from perfect. We tried all sorts of things to improve communications. The transducer, which both transmits and receives, was usually put overboard about 10 feet down. We tried letting out all the cable we had— about 75 feet—to see if there might be an improvement in getting below any of the thermal layer effects. I talked to Jim in the *Soucoupe*, but he could only occasionally understand me. Then the transducer cable suddenly went taut. I thought that some large denizen of the sea had perhaps decided to feed on it—but it was only caught under a rock on the bank. Carefully we worked it loose and recovered it. It was probably better off at just 10 feet under.

After about two hours we got word that the *Soucoupe* had dropped its weight and was on its way up. Jim described the dive as having been most exciting and successful. The bank was almost entirely covered with a pale-pink coral growth that completely obscured the geological structure. As the saucernauts got closer to the bank they noticed an increasing number of fish. There were schools of small, white, highly iridescent ones, with other schools of yellowtails and several large sheepshead. These swam among the fan-like gorgonian corals and encrusting bryozoan growths. The rocks had the long-spined black sea urchins commonly found in warmer water. In addition, the divers reported four moray eels, amber jack, and a large sting ray. Jim concluded by saying, "I got to see what I wanted to see—the walls of the bank and the bank itself—and it looks a natural site for the observatory."

Since we hadn't discussed this previously, my curiosity forced me to ask what NMC really had in mind.

"The way the design is shaping up at the moment," Jim said, "we're talking about a plastic acrylic sphere approximately 10 feet in diameter that would carry enough life support to keep two people going for a week. This way they could get some real observations over a period of time. We would probably moor the dwelling on the bottom but allow it to winch up and down so the observers could pick their level."

In the evening we returned briefly to San Clemente Island to disembark the observers of the last two days, then headed for San Nicolas Island 45 miles to the northwest where we had a date to dive for Pacific Missile Range. We arrived very early in the morning and lay to in a small uninviting harbor. By dawn a brisk breeze had built a choppy sea and was freshening to 25 knots. The possibility of diving looked unlikely for the next two days. Our observer/scientists from PMR, Bob Elzenga and Tom Henebry, joined us by small boat. They had flown from Point Mugu to the island base. We searched for a spot protected from the sea with its 4- to 5-foot-high waves. But there was no protection at San Nicolas, and it seemed best to go back to the southeast of Santa Catalina. Bob Elzenga, a Lieutenant in the Navy with a degree in geology, had wanted to examine the terrace-like features around San Nicolas Island, but the main mission of his dives could be accomplished on any smooth sandy bottom. So we turned stern to the wind and ran back to the protection of the inner islands.

The following day dawned gray, misty, with a nearly calm sea—occasionally the reddish sun broke through. It was Thanksgiving Day. Shortly after breakfast we could see that Little Joe was especially busy in the galley. It might not be a holiday for us, but we certainly couldn't go without a turkey dinner.

On deck preparations were nearly complete for the *Saucer* launch. Our newest crew member, Ken Lange, had recently arrived from Baltimore and was quickly taking over much of the routine *Saucer* servicing after each dive, the preparations before the next dive, and some of the maintenance, under the watchful eye of Gaston. The procedure consisted of filling the main batteries and propulsion motor seal with oil, charging oxygen and water ballast, and replacing iron weights for ascent and descent. Now Ken took over the responsibility for all routine preparations before each dive and recorded them on a pre-dive check list. He had joined our group after 22 years as a machinist in the Navy and specialist in underwater demolition (UDT).

For this dive I was to be the hookup diver. While I went below and got into my wet suit, the Navy team, including three or four ratings, was busy getting the experimental package prepared for launch. This was a specially designed pinger that had been procured at PMR. It gave out a signal on 9 KC and 45 KC. We placed a tunable pinger receiver in the *Saucer* so we could choose either frequency. Since Dive 231 we had managed to use a pinger successfully on several dives; we therefore felt that we could perform the day's dive. The pilot or observer could choose a frequency with the receiver and listen for either the 9 KC or 45 KC frequency signal. PMR was interested in experimenting with pingers and ways to home on signals. There were many requirements for the relocation of objects underwater, such as nose cones and missile parts. Today the array was planted at a spot several miles offshore and about 200 meters deep. A surface buoy was attached to the polypropylene line for recovery and visual reference. The *Saucer* was to be launched 700 meters from the buoy.

The ship moved away from the buoy and took up position. While we were waiting for the ship to come to a stop, the engineer and Little Joe spotted a small shark slowly cruising some distance away. This was the first shark we'd seen since we'd been working on the Pacific. It looked like a blue shark.

With Bob and Canoe buttoned up and the deck checkout complete, the *Saucer* was swung around and gently lowered into the water. Fred gave the usual tug on the release line and the *Saucer* hung easily on the tag line. He turned and said to me, "OK. In the water you go."

I jumped in close to the *Saucer* and started unscrewing the pins in the large shackles of the lifting bridle. There were three legs that attached to pad eyes and led to a ring about 8 inches in diameter made of 1-inch stock. The bridle weighed about 30 pounds in air and maybe 10 in water. The water temperature felt to be about 55 degrees F. I took the bridle to the small boat nearby and handed it to Larry. Then I waited while Gaston made his final check with Canoe over the hardwire phone. The conversation always ended with *"Bon— ciao!"* I looked around for the shark, but he (or she) was nowhere to be seen. Perhaps the bright-colored *Saucer* looked unfriendly. Gaston nodded to Fred that all was OK and Fred gave the disconnect sign since, with the ship's-generator noise, water in ears, etc., it was hard to hear. I slid in gently over the front of the *Saucer* to reach the hardwire-phone jack. We were always careful to avoid accidentally kicking a light or camera. I pulled the connector apart. Then I reached for the quick-release of the tag line and looked up at Fred. He motioned to let it go. I did. The *Saucer* was no longer part of our world—it was on its own. To speed it along, the diver usually climbs on top of the hatch, since his added weight helps break the surface tension and pushes the *Saucer* along. It was a good prop for a show-off. The *Saucer* sank beneath me and I remained watching it very slowly descend in the clear water. Then, when it was 15 or 20 feet down, it began to return to the surface. A moment later I heard Canoe over the radio in the small boat, "More weight, please."

He had slightly miscalculated and now needed additional weight to get down deep enough to where any trapped external air—such as that in the batteries—would be expelled; the *Saucer* would then descend normally. I swam back to the ship —about 25 yards—got a 7-pound lead weight and returned to the *Saucer* diving down to put the weight into the basket. I looked at Canoe through the port. He indicated that they needed one more weight. Another swim, for another 7 pounds. This time he gave me the thumb-up OK sign. I pushed the *Saucer* under again, this time for sure, and returned to the small boat. I had had my workout for this Thanksgiving.

After changing my wet suit I joined the tracking boat. We talked frequently to the *Saucer* and the communication was occasionally good. The saucernauts were apparently moving in the right direction but said they had trouble with the initial pinger contact. The variation in direction or azimuth was about 30 degrees, using the 9 KC source. They were traveling 7 or 8 meters off the bottom for best results. As they approached the pinger, the ping got stronger. After half an hour or so it was hard for us to tell what they were doing, and as it turned out, a series of mishaps occurred to confuse the issue completely. We, occupants of the small boat, had been tracking the 37 KC pinger fixed to the *Saucer,* but we could also hear the 9 and 45 KC array as we got closer to it, since our receiver picked up all of them. Suddenly the *Saucer* pinger speeded up drastically, then failed. We could hear the main propulsion motor, so we knew they were still moving. The telephone wouldn't work over the noise of the *Saucer* motor. Since we started tracking we had been using the buoy as reference, with occasional sights over toward the beach. Now a hazy mist had obscured the land. The ship had been lying-to drifting and was some distance away.

About this time Canoe found he had to change course several times and had overshot the array. The saucernauts knew they were closer by the strength of the signal. Larry finally gave up trying to stay with the *Saucer* after they changed course. By this time perhaps an hour and a half had gone by and we realized that the buoy was drifting. We told the *Hugh Tide* and they went to inspect it. The buoy float had come untied from the line to the pinger array. After an hour of repeated calling, we still had no communication with the *Saucer.* As we continued to call the usual "*Soucoupe . . . Soucoupe*" on the telephone, we suddenly heard the very familiar and startling whistle that Canoe used on the CB radio, followed by "Surface, surface, here is *Soucoupe* on surface." We did a double-take. The ship asked us where the *Saucer* was and we couldn't see it at all. The mist had become a uniform gray so that it was difficult to see the horizon.

"*Soucoupe, Soucoupe,* this is the tracking boat. We can't see you. Give us a shot of your water jets."

"Surface—*Soucoupe.* Can't make water jet. Motor is out."

Both we and the ship's crew searched and talked for at

least 15 minutes before we finally spotted them. The *Saucer* is only 6 to 10 inches high in the water if there is no sea motion. Although we found it without difficulty, this occurrence reminded us that we must always stay close by and be able to locate the *Saucer* under all conditions.

When the *Saucer* came aboard, it was discovered that the electric motor that drives the water jet pump had burned out. Bob Elzenga was disappointed that they had failed to find the pinger and even more so when he found that the loosely tied knot in the polypropylene line meant that he lost a $700 pinger. Certainly, we concluded at the debriefing, something was learned, but the art of pingers and homing on them had not been mastered.

Our lack of success was made up for shortly afterward as Little Joe announced that Thanksgiving Dinner was ready. He had put a splendid feast on the table for all 20 of us. Turkey, mashed potatoes, corn, cranberries, giblet gravy, and stuffing. Little Joe had started as a cook only several years earlier, after transferring from the deck department on a tugboat. He was a superb cook, a firm believer in cookbooks and recipes, and had a small library on board. Nothing seemed lacking in our Thanksgiving Day as we watched the annual football games on TV on our way to port.

Even Gaston, who was a most serious and dedicated worker, devoted to keeping the *Saucer* operating, took the afternoon off, saying he would dig into the *Soucoupe* innards in the evening. We were through with the *Hugh Tide* and were on our way to make the changeover to *Burch Tide* and much of the equipment, vans, and space we had been deprived of this past month.

In about 25 days we had made 20 dives, shaken down our routines, trained most of our inexperienced crew, and were now ready to move into high gear for the next set of dives and a quite different assignment.

CHAPTER 6

San Clemente

I awoke slowly to a new and unfamiliar motion and different surroundings. I remembered going off to sleep at about 2 AM amid the noise of activity on deck while the ship was at the fuel dock. My bunk was next to a window opening on a large alleyway on deck of the M/V *Burch Tide* and we were approaching the island of San Clemente. It was a new experience to awake looking out on deck—for I had always been berthed below on oceanographic ships.

This ship was no more than a barge, slightly pointed at the bow. The open deck area measured about 100 feet by 27 feet. On this we had attached our seven trailer-vans in two rows, forming a center aisle. Below us was a narrow passageway between a series of water tanks. The afterquarter of the ship was the engine room. The water tanks carried about 140,000 gallons and were normally used in part for ballast and part for fresh water or other liquids. The forward section of the ship contained a high wheelhouse, galley, and crew's quarters. With all the vans, painted Westinghouse blue, the large orange crane, and the yellow *Saucer* we were a strange and colorful sight. I lay in bed enjoying the luxury of sleeping late—we had at least another hour to go before arriving at San Clemente.

Over the weekend we had worked steadily to accomplish the transfer of all our equipment from the *Hugh Tide* to the *Burch Tide*. An enormous crane arrived to pick our own crane off one ship and place it on the other. As before, the marine inspector and insurance underwriter were present to see the installation and foundations. As we began to haul our supplies, consisting of weights, oils, CO_2 absorbent, tools, electronics, and so on, to the other ship, a separate welding crew started to place the new vans on the *Burch Tide*. We all worked late into both nights, and finally toward midnight the shift was complete. The *Hugh Tide* looked naked and forlorn, with scar marks on deck where things had been cut away.

The significant fact was that we had proved the Westinghouse concept—that the submersible diving operation we had designed was portable and could quickly be shifted from one ship to another or from beachhead to ship in a short time. It had taken less than 60 hours to make the changeover.

Amid all the activity of roustabouts, welders, movers, and the confusion of the weekend, Gaston had made the necessary repair to the *Saucer* motor. He discovered that an unused inspection plate had probably been the source of a leak that shorted the motor. Our underwater telephone, still not too dependable, was overhauled by the manufacturer, who found that much of the difficulty apparently stemmed from noisy pump motors, unshielded leads, and similar electrical conditions prevalent in the *Saucer*.

Now, as we drew near the island, I felt that we were in the best possible working order and ready for our new customer —the U.S. Naval Ordnance Test Station of Pasadena, California.

I strolled out on deck and up on the forward wing to see

what was ahead. San Clemente lay before us, stretching to the south as far as I could see. It rose steeply out of the ocean looking very fresh and barren, without a tree in sight—only rocks and steep slopes. The island is about 20 miles long and perhaps 6 miles across at the widest point. The hills rise to over 1,960 feet.

San Clemente Island is an ideal location for naval activities since it is a government reservation not open to the public. Further, deep water is very close to shore. One mile or so off-shore lies the full depth of 4,000 feet. Early experiments with the firing of Polaris missiles underwater had been accomplished here at a point some 5 miles from Wilson Cove. This was called the "Pop-Up" Site. A very elaborate test platform was implanted at a depth of 250 feet. It had a movable car on rails that simulated the motion of a submarine. On it a missile traveled and actual firings were made from it. As the missile broke the surface an enormous barge stood by with a crane and net. The "fish net" caught the missile as it rose out of the water. The Pop-Up Site was not in use now that the Polaris missile launching program had become fully operational.

Little Joe had his galley functioning for the first time to give us all a hearty breakfast. Normally the *Burch Tide* only provided for eight to twelve crew members when it was working for offshore oil companies. Four to six could eat in shifts in the small galley. Since our full crew at times numbered as many as 26 persons, the Tidewater Marine people had removed the bunks in the port quarters and converted it into a dining area and wardroom. At least ten of us could eat at one sitting, while the ship's crew continued to eat in the galley area. We had added a freezer in the dining wardroom as well as a television set for recreation. Curtains and pinup lamps, as well as "pinup" pictures that the crew put around, made it more livable.

Several of us sat around discussing the future dives. "I wonder what sort of things the Navy wants to do here," Joe Thompson said.

"They sent us an outline of an over-all plan," I told him, "that spoke of a lot of homing on pingers, lifting torpedoes, and working with crazy-looking devices. You know, they have an unmanned vehicle that seems to work well."

Our eggs arrived. About this time Gaston walked in, neatly dressed as usual, with a cheerful "*bonjour*" and a handshake for everyone.

"What would you like for breakfast, partner?" asked Little Joe. "How about some French toast?"

Gaston's eyes twinkled a little and he said jokingly, but still with a note of disdain, "French toast—but American bread. Thank you, no!" His usual fare was toast dipped in coffee. Sometimes Canoe had the same.

Suddenly there seemed to be great silence. The skipper had cut the engines and we were coasting along, probably close in to Wilson Cove now. I could hear shouts and engines of other boats backing down. From the wardroom it was hard to see what was going on outside, as there were only two ports. I went out on deck and saw a group from the Navy coming aboard. Who should be among them but our old friend, not long departed—André Laban. We had heard he was to return to help with piloting the *Saucer*. We expected to make a large number of dives and could use two pilots.

André always looked the part of a super-secret submarine commander, I thought, with his shaven head, a fur-collared short jacket, and leather boots. With him were several of the Navy men who would be diving during the next few days. André had flown out to San Clemente with them.

A number of us gathered in our new office—the end of the largest van, which had a round conference table, library, and meeting area. Howard Talkington, of the U.S. Naval Ordnance Test Station (NOTS), described the plan for the next two weeks. It was rigorous. He hoped to make two dives each day, to get experience in a small submersible for as many as possible in his group. In addition to short rides there were a number of fairly complex tasks involved. One of them was part of a simulated submarine rescue and was a direct result of the recommendations made by the Deep Submergence System Program (DSSP). The other part of the dive objectives involved adapting special hardware to the *Saucer* for the recovery of torpedoes and directional homing on pingers attached to torpedoes. Howard hoped that we could get some of the gadgetry operating during the first week, for a number of visitors from Washington would arrive the following week to dive with us and to see how things operated at San Clemente. NOTS hoped that this site could become an underwater test range for all sorts of submersible activity.

The kind of work we were planning fell mostly into the category of Ocean Engineering—that is, doing useful work in the ocean. Although several of the dives would be scientific, many were not. We looked forward to some of these new applications for a vehicle—but after seeing the schedule we wondered if we could perform the number of dives required. So far we had established a good record of the number of dives made compared to the amount of maintenance and equipment failure. The next two weeks would tell if we could make twice the number of dives.

The first dive got off uneventfully and met with little success. The plan was to inspect an underwater hydrophone at a depth of about 300 feet, but as happened before there was trouble hearing the pinger that operated on 9 kilocycles. Not until later that afternoon did we learn that through a misunderstanding the pinger that was controlled by the shore station had not been switched on. It seemed as though it took a dive or two to get everyone in step. Actually, I found that if the observer was going to make scientific observations and had not been in a small submersible before, it usually took two or perhaps even three dives for him to become fully accustomed to and acquainted with the arrangement and techniques. It was an unusual observer who could make valuable observations on the first dive. In this case, our observer was able to see a lot of the steeply sloping sandy bottom that surrounds San Clemente and to get a proper idea of working in a vehicle like the *Saucer.*

Early the next morning we went through our preparation check-out while taking up position near a large gray Navy ship that had been converted for special underwater work. I say "large" because anything bigger than the 136-foot *Burch*

Tide always seemed large to me. The vessel was designated a Yard Freight Utility (YFU) and had a long center well open to the sea. We would be working close to it today and the *Saucer* was to perform several tasks together with the YFU.

The observer was Ed Carpenter and I showed him through the *Saucer*, as I had begun to do for each new person. I showed him where the camera controls were and how to read the depth gauge and use the telephone. During these pre-dive orientations I usually learned what the observer wanted to accomplish. If the dive sounded more complicated than a normal one I tried to get the pilot to discuss the special requirements. Ed Carpenter was the first of several NOTS divers who wished to see if the *Saucer* could perform the delicate maneuvers necessary to simulate a submarine rescue. Before commencing the dive he described the situation to André. The YFU was moored between three buoys in 842 feet of water. From this position a framework was lowered through the center well on four cables. This frame was equipped with several lights, TV cameras, a 35mm still camera and strobe, and hydrophones. In the center had been placed a circular cradle exactly like the one that the *Soucoupe* normally rests in. Alongside was a spear some 6 feet long, which the *Saucer* was supposed to pick up after it sat in the cradle. The maneuver was the hard part: to place the end of the spear through a bail or loop on a mock-up submarine hatch. This technique simulated one now standard in the Navy for attaching a McCann rescue chamber to a disabled submarine. To date the procedure could not be carried out at depths greater than 800 feet.

We launched Ed and André about 150 yards from the YFU. Val was the duty diver in the water and Jerry and I went out in the tracking boat. After 20 minutes or so it was plain that the *Saucer* was steering right for the YFU, so Jerry and I requested permission to go aboard the latter and watch the show on television.

"No problem," radioed Fred from the *Burch Tide*. "If we hear anything we'll call you at the YFU."

Aboard, we walked up and down and around a maze of catwalks without seeing anyone. We found that everyone was in the control room crowded around several TV monitors. At first I was reminded of a movie I had seen of a missile launching and the scene in the blockhouse. All around us were technicians in white coveralls; an enormous set of consoles with TV screens was on one side. Radios squawked, the two controllers pushed buttons and gave orders, while lights flashed.

Then, just after we arrived, the *Saucer* came faintly into view on the screen. There was an underwater telephone set aboard the YFU which worked on the same 42-kilocycle frequency. The communication was excellent today. The saucernauts had been able to steer by the floodlight from the frame and had seen it from a distance of at least 100 meters. Now André brought the *Saucer* slowly in over the frame, making a high pass to inspect it and watch the motion as it surged. The swell on the surface was sufficient to make the platform move up and down, occasionally touching bottom on one corner. The surge was a foot in the vertical. The *Saucer* then turned and started back in toward the cradle. Every one of the 25 or 30 people watching was sure that this time André would settle the *Saucer* down into the cradle. But even something that seems as simple as resting on the cradle is not easy. It takes a delicate control of the slow-speed switch and ballast control. We could hear the motor go on and off over the telephone. Then André had to ballast just enough water in at the right moment to settle. If there was any current, the procedure became more difficult. I held my breath and watched. The *Saucer* hung with the bow down. We couldn't understand what was going on. It stayed in this position for several minutes. Next Carpenter transmitted: "We've just dropped our weight and are coming up."

Jerry and I moved out through the crowd to get the boat, wondering what was wrong. In a little while we heard clearly on our telephone in the boat.

"Hallo—small boat, here is *Soucoupe*. We are coming up slowly. We have no jets. Over."

From a depth of 840 feet it took over half an hour for the *Saucer* to reach the surface. Since it had no propulsion, André had taken on water in the water tank to decrease the buoyancy and to ascend slowly in order to be sure not to come up under the YFU. The saucernauts surfaced well away from the vessel, where the *Burch Tide* could maneuver to pick them up.

"Poor Gaston," Jerry said. "He'll probably have more work to do on the *Saucer*."

We saw Gaston standing on the stern of the *Burch Tide* watching the *Saucer* as Joe swung it aboard. He looked at it as though he thought all we ever did was break it on each dive.

A short time later I heard Larry telling someone in the aisle, "It was only the hoses that attach to the Y connector. They must have loosened and come off since the rebuilding of the motor last week. No problem."

All of us had picked up some of the phrases that Canoe and Gaston used. By far the most common was "no problem." It became our byword and motto over the next weeks and months.

Our second dive of the day was late in getting off, even though the first, No. 252, had been short. Preparation always seemed to take at least an hour longer than any of us anticipated. Thus the hookup diver of the day would be suited up waiting for things to happen and getting unpleasantly warm on deck. No matter how hard the rest of us tried to speed things along, it wasn't possible to hurry Gaston, who would be carefully checking some small part.

I was to take a second crack at the small boat along with Larry. I had checked out Commander Crowder inside the *Saucer* earlier. He was a submarine commander and fairly familiar with the ways of diving boats, so we hadn't taken long. I stopped to see how Joe Thompson was doing with the cameras. It was his job to make sure that the two cameras on the *Saucer* were loaded properly, connected, batteries charged, as well as to take care of many other details of the photographic gear that we used for documentary shots. He had been a big help in trying to keep our scientist divers pleased during the delicate times. We would find out, for example, that the film had jammed in the Edgerton camera and

The *Diving Saucer* makes its appearance at Los Alamitos Naval Air Station on its way to join our team in November 1964. The *Saucer* was flown directly from Marseilles, France, by a MATS C-124c Cargomaster. (*Thompson*)

Top view of the *Saucer* at launch time. While the *Saucer* is held by the tag line, the diver removes the lifting bridle and prepares to let it go. Gaston Roux talks on the hardwire telephone to the pilot. As soon as the Operations Officer gives the OK, the diver disconnects the phone line and the tag line and pushes the *Saucer* under. (*Thompson*)

The MV *Burch Tide*, a 136-foot oil-well service vessel that Westinghouse used to support the diving saucer. The 100-by-27-foot deck space accommodates seven trailer-type vans, the hydraulic crane, and the *Saucer*, making a portable diving service. (*Westinghouse*)

Dr. Francis P. Shepard of Scripps Institution of Oceanography, distinguished marine geologist, holds a sextant that he used frequently for near-shore positioning prior to a dive in *La Soucoupe*. (*Church*)

Canoe poses momentarily in sweater and wool diving cap before closing the 15¾-inch hatch and beginning another dive for scientific investigation. (*Church*)

Fred Willett holds the release line for the automatic hook ready to release the *Saucer,* suspended from the bridle. The *Saucer* will then be held by the nylon tag line for check-out in the water. (*Thompson*)

The *Saucer's* view ports allow occupants to obtain a full view of about 120 degrees. Note the small port in the middle for the movie camera mounted inside. The rack beneath the ports holds the expendable ballast weights. (*Church*)

The *Soucoupe* hovers near the surface about to start its voyage into the canyons — looking more like a spacecraft than a submarine. (*Church*)

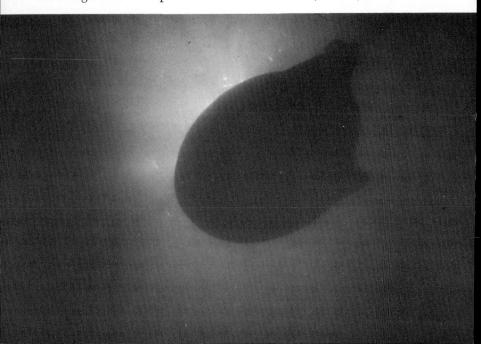

The tracking boat, *Shazam,* in action over the submerged *Saucer.* One man operates the "pinger tracker," one shoots local landmarks with a sextant for bearing fixes, while the third communicates over the underwater telephone to the *Saucer* and drives *Shazam.* (*Church*)

A good example of ripples formed in the sandy sediments along the bottom of the San Lucas Canyon. (*Dill*)

A beer can and an older can found lying on the canyon floor on a dive by Dr. R. F. Dill. These cans show that there has been little accumulation of sediments in the canyon floor at this point. In other areas partly buried cans indicate a movement of sediment in the canyon. (*Dill*)

A *Saucer* photo showing the contact between canyon wall and the sediment on the floor. The lower part of the wall is freshly exposed where a portion of the sediment has been moved out recently in San Lucas Canyon. (*Dill*)

Debris and small pieces of wood and material found in Los Frailes Canyon as evidence of a strong movement down the canyon during flooding. Such debris is moved along with the sediments in a down-canyon direction into deeper water. (*Dill*)

The *Saucer* comes across one of its own 55-pound weights that it had dropped earlier. Notice how the weight has buried itself in the soft sediment. Two of these weights are dropped on each dive. They are considered expendable and are worth about $20.00. (*Dill*)

The *Diving Saucer* is picked out of the water by the crane on the support ship. Water from free-flooded areas pours out, and the *Saucer* will be swung around and placed on board. (*Church*)

The *Diving Saucer* is brought aboard the *Burch Tide* by the crane as the author steadies it. (*Thompson*)

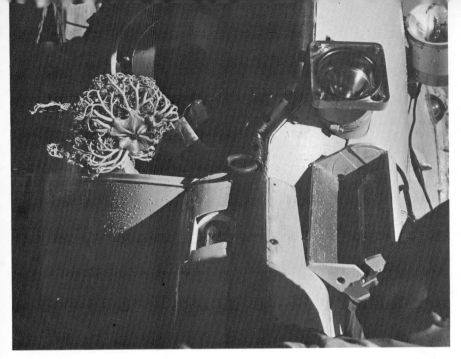

The *Saucer* captures a basket star with its mechanical claw and returns it in the sample basket. Note the lights for movie, floodlights, and general lights. (*Westinghouse*)

André Laban, one of the *Saucer* pilots, inspects a variety of basket star with branching arms. (*Church*)

The Savonious current meter with the plastic rotor. On top of it is the temperature sensor. To the left is the special penetrator, with a molded cable entering through a steel shank into the interior of the *Saucer* hull. The funnel-shaped device at the far left holds the tracking pinger. (*Thompson*)

The *Saucer* water-propulsion pump and motor drive are removed for repair after the motor burned out. Gaston Roux holds the pump, which is driven by the 2-HP dc motor that moves the *Saucer* along at nearly one knot. (*Thompson*)

The *Saucer* fitted out with a "slurp gun." Dr. Carl Hubbs of Scripps Institution of Oceanography tried out a pump device developed by NEL to suck up small fish observed in La Jolla Canyon, for study and identification. (*Westinghouse*)

The author (left) and Joe Thompson prepare to make a dive using scuba equipment. During this dive they descended with the *Saucer* off La Jolla, California, to a depth of 175 feet. On a single tank of compressed air they were limited to about nine minutes at that depth, while the *Saucer* explorers enjoyed nearly four hours to depths of 1,000 feet. (*Thompson*)

A cause for celebration. We carry on the French tradition of celebrating every 50th dive. Dive 300 finds us in Mexico diving for Dr. Douglas Inman of Scripps Institution of Oceanography at Los Frailes. Standing: Fred Willett, Larry Somers, Val Boeleskeny, Ken Lange, Ned Shenton. Jerry Burnett, pilot "Canoe" Kientzy, Gaston Roux, Dr. Inman, and Joe Thompson.

The elaborate cake that "Little Joe" made for the celebration of Dive 300. The *Diving Saucer* model was also a cake, with marshmallows for lights, licorice for bumper rails, bottle caps for ports. (*Church*)

A typical calm day at Cabo San Lucas, Mexico, as the *Diving Saucer* is being brought in on the tag line for retrieval by the crane. (*Church*)

The *Saucer* hangs poised for a dive using the U.S. Navy Underwater Sound Laboratory acoustic array. These seven hydrophones mounted on a 15-foot boom were used to measure ambient sea noise and show the feasibility of a submersible for a "quiet" platform. (*Westinghouse*)

The acoustic array with seven hydrophones geometrically spaced is fitted to the *Saucer* by Edward April of the U.S. Navy Underwater Sound Laboratory, while Jacques "Gaston" Roux scrutinizes the arrangement. (*U.S. Navy photo*)

Jacques-Yves Cousteau visits his men while on business in San Diego. Jacques "Gaston" Roux, in the hatch, listens while Raymond "Canoe" Kientzy describes one of our dives for science. (*U.S. Navy photo*)

Westinghouse pilot trainees and original *Deepstar* team members ready for a dive. Joe Thompson (left) and Larry Somers both were trained as pilots. Joe did much of the underwater photography involving the *Saucer*, and Larry Somers was team diving officer. (*Westinghouse*)

The author stands in the hatch of the *Soucoupe* before making a dive in Cabo San Lucas. All members of the *Deepstar* team got at least one orientation dive during the six-month operation. (*Church*)

We celebrate our 100th dive on *Saucer* '65 as "Little Joe," the cook, serves champagne to Canoe, the pilot. It was also the day of the first Gemini flight, March 23, 1965. (*Westinghouse*)

Joe Thompson sits patiently while ship's barber and *Saucer* pilot, André Laban, trims. (*Church*).

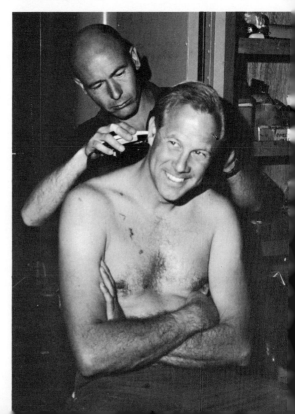

all those beautiful shots that the scientist thought he had gotten were ruined. Photography for the scientific dives and the resulting pictures were among the most important data, for they were the evidence of what each man had seen and needed later for further examination and documentation.

"I don't know what else to do," Joe sighed as we stood talking in the photo van. "The still camera has been intermittent this week. Sometimes it works fine, but then the strobe doesn't always fire. I found the connector flooded after one dive and then the contacts were very dirty the next time in the camera mechanism. It seems we just have to check constantly to see that it's working."

The Edgerton camera had been made especially for Captain Cousteau by his old friend and undersea colleague, Dr. Harold Edgerton. Dr. Edgerton was affectionately known as "Papa Flash" by Cousteau, and was Professor of Electrical Engineering at M.I.T. The camera was built in 1958 and was the prototype of a well-known model now used the world over by oceanographers for deep-sea photography. Ours had taken many photographs and now required a certain amount of care and understanding to keep it operating. For this series of dives at San Clemente photography was of minor importance; nevertheless, Joe worked hard to have everything in top working order.

As we got close to launching time Joe's activities increased; the cameras had to be installed. The 16mm movie camera went inside, then the pilot would run some footage while Joe held a board with the dive number on it for later identification. Next the still camera was put in its place outside and connected. The pilot then fired several shots with it to see if the strobe light was operating and putting out a full-strength flash. The dive number on this camera was recorded automatically on each frame.

By this time Fred would be asking Joe to man the crane to put the vehicle in the water, just when he would have liked to be making some coverage of the dive for a movie sequence. This was Joe's frustration. He was determined, however, that somewhere during our six months of diving he would film

enough footage to make a complete movie of our undertaking.

Now, as we were finally ready to go, I saw Fred hesitating
and squinting at the sun sinking deep in the west almost behind the high ridge of the island's hills.

"I think we'd be smart to put the flashing light on, Jerry. It
will most certainly be dark by the time we recover the *Saucer*," advised Fred.

Jerry bounded into the electronics van, which was still only
half of the photo van. He picked up a rod with a small light
encapsulated on the end. This was a xenon flash tube potted
in epoxy that could be turned on from inside the *Saucer*.
It gave out a high-intensity flash for night recognition.

Jerry usually performed most of the routine electrical jobs
on the *Saucer*. Although the present task was only a matter of
making a plug in the connection, it was important that it be
done correctly. Gaston, as usual, stood by watching.

The flasher was attached and Commander Crowder disappeared in the *Saucer* followed by Canoe. The *Saucer* was
launched seaward of the hydrophone array with the 9-KC
pinger. Crowder was going to make another run on the mission that had proven unsuccessful yesterday. He was familiar
with this area off San Clemente as one of the pilots of the
Navy vehicle *Moray*. *Moray* was a torpedo-shaped 2-man vehicle built by NOTS; it had a high-speed propulsion, no view
ports, and a great amount of complicated instrumentation.
The Navy had been developing it as an experimental vehicle.

Larry and I were joined by Joe Berkich of NOTS, who
wanted to see how we tracked the *Saucer*. We could hear the
steady beep of the 37-KC tracking pinger as the *Saucer* descended. The water depth at launching was 220 meters. Very
soon the sun set and we were about half a mile offshore in the
shadow of the steep cliffs. We bobbed around in the 17-foot
whaler, keeping station directly over the *Saucer*. After about
12 to 15 minutes I figured that the saucernauts were on the
bottom and expected them to begin moving inshore toward
the hydrophone installation.

"Small boat, this is *Burch Tide*," our CB radio squawked.

"Go ahead, *Burch Tide.*"

"The shore station reports they have turned on the 9-KC pinger with a modulated signal. They want to know when Commander Crowder can hear it."

"OK. We'll ask him by and by." I returned, knowing that the observer had probably just gotten started and would only be disturbed by our call on the telephone.

A chilly sea wind had sprung up. There was a bit of nip in the air. Our position was being plotted by a radar station farther down the island as the approximate location of the *Saucer.* From this position we would try to direct the *Saucer* toward the target if the saucernauts were having trouble in determining the direction of the hydrophone in 100 meters of water.

I let a few more minutes go by, then began to try to raise the *Saucer* occupants.

"*Soucoupe, Soucoupe,* this is the small boat . . . the small boat. Can you hear us? Come back." I waited for a moment and could hear the hiss and static and bits of noise in the water. In the background Larry thought he heard the *Saucer's* motor. I tried the call again. Perhaps the divers were listening for the pinger and had turned the telephone receiver down. This was a favorite trick of André's when he was engaged in some delicate maneuver. In a way I sympathized—still we believed the telephone receiver should always be left on in case of emergency. Many times the surface boat would merely stand by and wait for a message rather than call.

We noted that the *Soucoupe* was moving inshore slowly but in a SW direction instead of W. We were getting frequent plots from the radar station that showed us to be closing the distance yet still off course. We attempted to pass this information on to the *Saucer* but received no acknowledgment. I could see that Joe Berkich wasn't impressed with our telephone communications although it had been far better in the morning. About 45 minutes had passed since launch with no telephone contact. The course had changed and we were sure the saucernauts were heading back out to sea! This time Larry tried calling. We stopped the boat and shut off the engine, called several times and listened. Nothing but the dull hissing. It was now getting quite dark and as always when you can't see far it seemed that the sea is making up more. We turned on our stern light on a staff and checked with Fred on the *Burch Tide* about half a mile away to make sure he saw us. He did.

"Let me give that crazy telephone a try," said Joe, "Maybe I can get hold of old man Crowder."

"Hello *Soucoupe*, hello *Soucoupe*, this is Captain Marvel, Captain Marvel. Can you read me?"

Joining in, Larry added a loud "Shazam"—the secret password of Captain Marvel of comic-book days. To our great amusement, the answer came back over the phone loud and clear.

"Captain Marvel, this is the *Soucoupe*. We have just found the cable of the hydrophone and are proceeding to follow it. Dive going well."

I relayed the information to the *Burch Tide*, feeling relieved that we had finally gotten through. But I was more amused at the incident of "Shazam." We needed a good code name for the small boat that we could use on the radio and in communications. Rather than having a single name and station numbers as they had at San Clemente we liked a separate name for each station. We had already become accustomed to hearing "Niceskater," which identified all the stations, ships, and vehicles on the island.

"That's it, then," agreed Larry, "Shazam it'll be for the small boat. As soon as we get ashore I'll buy some decal letters and put them on the stern."

We tracked the *Saucer* in the darkness for the next half hour, feeling the wind pick up slightly. We bounced around on a mounting sea, wondering what the retrieval would be like in the dark. Later we heard over the telephone that the saucernauts had dropped their weight. We passed the information to the *Burch Tide* and proceeded in to pick up the duty diver. Then we returned to our station and listening once more could hear both the pinger and the up-sonar. All of us peered below, wondering who would see the *Saucer* first and how close we might be.

"I think it's almost below us there," Jerry exclaimed, pointing.

"No, isn't that a reflection from the light on the *Burch Tide?*"

Before we could say anything more, the light turned into a pale white and yellow object making the water glow all around. It emerged some 8 feet from us with a gentle splash, the beacon flashing and the small headlights on. The *Saucer* was a strange and wondrous sight at night. Before Canoe could grab the radio microphone and call, Jerry had the tow bridle hooks on and was ready to attach the lifting bridle. Pretty good tracking, we thought. The *Saucer* was easily recovered and soon after we were all sitting around the debriefing table listening to Commander Crowder's report.

"We were down at some 220 meters and I figured you had put us outside instead of inside the array. So then we kept going 270 degrees and getting set south, so we came around to north and then 050 degrees and picked up the cable and followed it all around."

"What's the condition of the cable?" asked Howard Talkington.

"It's lying on the bottom, but there's so much slack that it's twisted, kinked, and has loops in it. Finally we came on the transducer. I got some photographs of the whole setup. It's clean and looks fine."

Canoe added, "There is a cable going up."

"Oh, yes," said Crowder, "We saw a line snagged on the power cable that disappeared going up to a float."

André asked, "Did you hear the transducer first or see the cable?"

"I think we heard the transducer first. We were going in a circle to see where the tone was loudest. In the last ten minutes we could pick it up clearly off toward the northeast. So we started out in that direction and sighted the cable two or three minutes later.

"What was the bottom like and the slope?" I queried.

"It was mostly sand."

"No rocks?"

"No, just sand. There was a dropoff at about—I'd say 160 meters—a very steep wall. The sand ends and it turned to pure rock."

"Were these rock outcrops?"

"Yes, I would say so—there wasn't any rock just lying there. The sand ended very abruptly where the rocks start. I guess the slope is 30 degrees or so."

"Did you see many animals?"

"Fish, starfish, a couple crabs, but no sponges. All in all it was successful since we're the first to see the transducer installation. I'd say that someone ought to do something about all that snagged cable before it gets worse."

This wound up our debriefing session and we all headed for chow hall. Later on in the evening the *Deepstar* gang was invited to see the *Moray* in its shop on the island. Our normal evening recreation at San Clemente was a walk up the hill—about 1,000 feet in the vertical—to the PX for three-week-old magazines and candy bars. If there was a good movie we would take it in. These movies were occasionally first-run, but sometimes of course they were awful; though for 15 cents you really couldn't complain. Tonight we'd missed the movie, but the chance to look at the *Moray* was a welcome change.

The *Moray* submarine had been a project of NOTS for several years and was now operational for various experimental programs. Many of the design features we noted resembled aircraft technology and concepts. The pilots sat side-by-side in one sphere that was fully packed with instruments, gauges, and controls. A second aluminum sphere was forward and contained electronics instruments entirely. With the aid of a forward scanning sonar the pilots "flew" the *Moray*, driven by several specially designed propellers on the stern. We gathered that it made fairly high speed. The batteries were placed in a separate container behind the 2-man pressure hull. The whole vehicle was vastly different from ours. It didn't dive by dropping weights but by pushing itself down, always maintaining positive buoyancy for a safety factor.

Larry and Joe climbed inside as one of the pilots sat on top and described all the controls. Looking in through the hatch I saw that little room was left after the two of them settled in place. On all sides were gauges, switches, and more switches. For most instruments and functions there was a second or back-up unit. The *Moray* appeared well planned, but certainly highly complex. I thought how simple the *Saucer* seemed in comparison yet how effective it had been already in over 250 dives. One of the interesting things about the submersible business is the fact that no two vehicles are alike and there is a wide diversity of concepts about designing, building, and operating underwater. We left the *Moray* hangar impressed with the "aircraft" approach to a submarine but more convinced than ever that the simple solution was equally valid.

The following day was stormy and gray, with a brisk northwesterly wind whipping up the waves to 3 or 4 feet beyond Wilson Cove. The schedule called for a collaboration of the *Saucer* and the NOTS CURV (Cable-controlled Underwater Recovery Vehicle). We moved up the island to a protected cove where it was possible to launch and retrieve without trouble.

CURV, a strange-looking device, had started out as an unmanned vehicle built by Vare Industries that NOTS had later modified for torpedo recovery. It was a propelled framework with buoyancy tanks and was controlled from the surface by cable. It carried a television camera, a 35mm camera, a scanning sonar, and lights.

Those of us not involved with launching or tracking watched the *Saucer* through the television on CURV from the support ship.

Much of the hour-and-a-half dive was spent by the *Saucer* crew observing the characteristics of the tether cable. Will Foreman was the observer. He was the pilot of *Deep Jeep,* another NOTS submersible being developed and which we were to see later. The *Saucer* also moved around as a target to determine the sensitivity of the scanning sonar on CURV.

We watched as the *Saucer* glided toward the CURV and its TV camera. So long as the bottom wasn't stirred up by the jets we could see quite clearly. As it got closer we could recognize André peering out the port. He had been reminded over the telephone not to turn on any bright lights, for they could damage the TV camera vidicon tube. In the monitor we could see André blink his eye. How marvelous a device, this TV! The most impressive feat of the day was a bit of Hollywood drama for all viewers. The *Saucer* moved in toward CURV, looking as "other-worldly" as a space ship, and extended its claw arm to the latter. The CURV operator, returning the formality, opened the large jaw of the torpedo grabber and the two snapped and groped like strange articulated beasts in a science-fiction movie. Finally, a momentary handshake was accomplished. It was surely "the day the monsters met at 50 fathoms."

We had no dive scheduled for the afternoon and the weather looked more blustery than ever, so a half holiday was declared. Several of us, including the *Deepstar* crew, Canoe, André, and Gaston, had been eager to see something of San Clemente. John Theisen, who worked for Photosonics, a contractor on the island for the Navy, offered to show us around. He had been out here working as an underwater photographer for nearly four years and like the rest of the Navy and civilian employees (about 150 of them) commuted by air each week to and from Long Beach. John borrowed two four-wheel pick-up trucks and we all loaded aboard with cameras, knapsacks, and hiking shoes. We drove up the steep hill past the barracks, mess hall, and motor pool. The terrain was extremely rocky and the peaks of the hills several hundred feet above us were partly veiled in mist. Low-flying scudding clouds moved rapidly by. The road wound along through a boulder-strewn valley and up over a series of round, bare hills. Looking to the east, we could see out over the ocean some distance below covered with "white horses" whipped up by the wind. The hills had a greenish look from a distance, but there was no vegetation to be seen close by. On the right there was a small green sign posted, "You are now entering San Clemente National Forest." Sure enough, there were five struggling eucalyptus trees neatly planted alongisde the road.

As far as I could tell these were the only trees on the entire island. John Theisen took pleasure in showing visitors about the island and said that this was one of the high spots of the trip. Fifty yards after the entrance a second sign announced that we had just left San Clemente National Forest. John said most people weren't sure whether he was joking or whether this was a real attempt at forestry. Shortly after the "forest" the road turned to dirt and became considerably rougher. John reported to "Niceskater 1," the main radio control station, to say that we were going down the island. This area was normally restricted, not so much because of military activity, but because it became so inaccessible that people going off for a hike or exploring had become stranded, lost, or injured.

We were now working down to the west of the island, out of the hills down nearer the water. A long rocky and debris-strewn beach stretched for miles toward the northwest corner of the island. It looked covered with driftwood and shells.

"That beach is sure great for combing and picking up things," John commented. "Everything tossed off ships bound for Hawaii and the rest of the Pacific seems to wash up there. Last year we found a perfectly good scuba tank farther up toward the point. If we have time we'll stop on the way back."

There was a heavy surf booming in at places that would certainly interest any surfer. The breeze was fresh and invigorating and occasionally a patch of afternoon sun broke through to make the scene more picturesque. The path now led bumpily up into the hills that rose in imposing grandeur, topped by the low clouds—uninhabited and untouched. Far away I could see numerous tiny specks on a steep hillside. As we got closer, they turned out to be great herds of reddish-brown wild goats that all but overran parts of the island. We were more than half a mile away and moving slowly, but they bolted and ran, leaping among the higher rocks to keep their distance. Their coats were long and shaggy. We never could get close to them, although they are reputed to be quite tame in some parts of the island.

Everywhere the ground was brown and dry, covered with

fragments of rock that had rolled down from the large out-crops. Much of it was covered with a greenish lichen. Small cactus abounded. Finally the lead truck pulled up to a bluff that we had been ascending for some time. We got out and stretched and brushed off the dust.

I walked toward the edge of the bluff and looked over. It dropped away in an almost sheer face. Three or four hundred feet below, at the edge of the surf, lay the enormous pinnacle of a rock completely covered with seals. There were tan seals and brown ones, and even a few white ones, basking in the afternoon sun that had now broken fully through the clouds. We all sat and took in this sight. The barking of the seals, mixed with the roar of the surf, drifted faintly up to us. Look-ing out to sea, the western Pacific stretched out to where it seemed to bend over the horizon. The ocean was speckled with patches of dark and light from occasional cloud shadows and wind-ruffles. It was the real, open Pacific Ocean. A long swell with breakers 8 to 10 feet high crashed upon the rocky cliffs below us. Occasionally several seals would playfully tus-sle and roll off into the water. There must have been a least a thousand animals in sight. I saw some that came around the big rock and swam into the surf where long rollers came into a short beach. These seals were actually riding in on the waves and having a wonderful time. Then Canoe nudged Gaston and pointed; close by to the surfing seals several large fins were cutting back and forth in the water.

"Those are Orca, the killer whale," André stated. "They will devour those seals!" I had read tales of killer whales being among the most ferocious and fearless predators alive. They would presumably make short work of an animal the size of a seal. There were accounts of killer whales devouring sea lions in one gulp. A sea lion is no small beast.

There were clearly three whales weaving slowly back and forth in the water, so close to the seals that it could only be a matter of moments before one was gobbled up. But nothing happened.

"Why don't the seals get out of there?" Jerry asked. John joined us, and we pointed out the situation. "Doesn't it look as though the seals were trapped in this little pocket?" we asked.

"Don't worry about the seals," he assured us. "They're in shallow water—too shallow for the killer whale, who knows he'd be stranded if he tried to move in after them. Of course, if one of the seals ventures out farther, then it's curtains for him."

We were relieved. The seals looked too friendly and happy at their play to be sacrificed.

After leaving Seal Cove, we bounced along in the truck to the beach to do some beachcombing at the foot of the cliff filled with caves that extened back into the volcanic mass. André and Gaston led us around some fascinating tidal pools on the rocky beach, picking out rare delicacies, to which they gave French names. These were mostly mussels and other bivalves that live in between Pacific tides. With delight Gaston prepared these morsels while Canoe and André sampled. He offered me one, which I took with great expectation of some rare new experience. To my surprise it was quite bitter, though still palatable, and certainly had a sea flavor. I declined another, however, on the grounds that one was enough.

We ventured into the mouth of a small cave nearby. It narrowed and continued far back into hillside. Unfortunately, we hadn't thought to bring flashlights. The cave looked interesting. We had already found numerous signs of the Indians who had lived on the island: great mounds of shells and other typical Indian remains of kitchen middens. Perhaps in the cave there might even have been artifacts. But in the now-gathering twilight it was too late to venture further. We trudged back to the trucks and as we started we heard a strange roar coming up the island. We expected to see a big truck, but next thing we knew a helicopter whirled overhead, shining a bright spotlight down on us. John said it was merely the patrol checking up. He called in to "Niceskater 1" to say we were heading back.

Our island excursion had been a welcome respite from the diving routine and a stimulating break for all.

We completed a total of 15 dives for NOTS in the two-week period. This was twice the number of normal dives, but most of them had been for short periods, to allow as many persons as possible to get a ride. We had only a maximum of about four hours on a battery charge so two dives of one-and-a-half or two hours were the limit. The dives in the following week were for the visiting dignitaries from the Special Projects Office of the Navy. We went through the same type of torpedo recovery and rescue simulation that we had practiced the week before, but with much more success.

Perhaps the best dive took place on the following Wednesday. The plan called for the *Saucer* to carry below the torpedo-lifting device from the surface. Earlier attempts resulted in various mishaps, so everyone was trying his hardest to do things right. NOTS had designed and built a small, light, two-claw harness to be dropped over a torpedo. On it was an electrically fired hydrazine gas generator and an inflatable lifting bag. Once started, the gas was generated in the bag, giving it a hundred pounds of lift. The *Saucer* held the device in the mechanical arm as it left the surface. A pull-away plug was connected to leads into the *Saucer* where a switch closed the contacts. Val had devised the technique for attaching the device to the *Saucer* in the water. Once the vehicle reached the bottom the pilot had to home on a 37-KC pinger (we'd given up on the 9 KC finally) which was on the dummy torpedo near the frame of the YFU 53. Again a large crowd, probably twice the size of that of last week, gathered before TV monitors in the control room aboard the YFU. The *Saucer* soon loomed into view on the screen, heading for the torpedo. The crew had reported that the pinger receiver was working satisfactorily. Canoe approached the torpedo, slowly planning his maneuvers, which involved aligning the claw device with the long axis parallel to the torpedo. Close timing and quick reflexes were required to position, lower, and release the device at the moment the switch for igniting the gas generator was closed.

This done, the *Saucer* would begin to back slowly away and

rise as the loss in weight changed the buoyancy. Canoe paused, then turned the *Soucoupe* a slight amount. Now shifting the mercury forward as the bow dipped down, he neatly placed the two claws over the torpedo. Simultaneously he fired the gas generator and released the arm's grip on the device. Once before André had done this, but the lifting bag did not have enough buoyancy. This time we all waited eagerly to see the result. The *Saucer* had moved partly off the screen. It took almost a minute for the bag to fill. Gradually we could see the torpedo moving and finally it broke free of the bottom. It was on its way to the surface. Everyone cheered, as if a major missile had been fired. The YFU public-address system proudly announced that we would soon see the torpedo surface about 50 feet to port. A small surface craft stood by. All the Navy brass crowded the rails of the ship, watching the spot. A few minutes went by. Certainly by now we should have seen the torpedo. Suddenly there was a shout from the well deck.

"Here it is, right in the well!" yelled Joe Berkich.

The red and white lifting bag had silently emerged in the well section of the YFU directly above the frame. Beneath was the torpedo. Canoe couldn't have done better. A perfect recovery.

With a second portion of the dive to go, he brought the *Saucer* in over the frame and quickly set it down on the nest, which had now been replaced by a rubber tire. From the forward TV camera we could watch the arm reach out and the claw open above the spear. It closed solidly, firmly grasping it. Now came the difficult part. The *Saucer* had to move forward a few feet and place the spear through a bail loop several inches wide. The first time Canoe missed altogether. Moving the *Saucer* and then stopping was a difficult maneuver. The second time Canoe went forward carefully—aiming. This time the spear went through. More topside cheers. This was a real first in submarine maneuvering. None of the other vehicles that we knew had been able to perform this feat with such precision. That afternoon a repeat performance was put on by André under more adverse conditions. He had a current of 0.3 knot and still managed to retrieve the torpedo successfully.

At the end of the week we departed San Clemente feeling as though we had made a significant accomplishment in the over-all operation of the *Diving Saucer*. The individual piloting feats of Canoe and André were most impressive and made the series of dives an outstanding success. At the same time we had gained valuable experience as a working team. We felt one step further along in our development of a diving service. The support effort and integrated facility aboard were going to pay off.

Next we would make a number of local dives and then prepare for our major expedition of the contract—the trip to Baja California. Truly the best was yet to come.

CHAPTER 7

On to Mexico

As time drew on toward Christmas everyone hoped for a little bad weather and a chance to get a day off for shopping. The weather remained fine, however, and each day we completed another dive in the La Jolla area. The scientists were from both Scripps and NEL and we alternated between biologists and geologists on successive dives.

If the scientist-observer was new to him, Canoe would first ascertain whether he was a biologist or geologist, because this dictated the general nature of the dive. Usually the biologist would have plotted on a chart the general course that he wanted to follow for investigating and making photographs. Canoe would then concentrate on fish, not rocks. This sometimes meant chasing after rare specimens and listening to the frustrated biologist, who wished so fervently that he could reach out and capture one of those creatures as the scuba diver could. Later in the spring the scientists developed a system whereby the small fish could be immobilized in order to collect them.

Even more than the geologist, the ichthyologist depended on photographs as his chief form of data. One of the problems for the scientist was to estimate the size of fish and other organisms. This could be done in a rough way with the still camera, which had two lenses, although I doubt that the camera was ever intended for the modification Joe made. It was possible to make a delicate mechanical adjustment to the near-focus lens so that both lenses were focused approximately together. We then had a stereo camera focused at about 32 inches instead of a pair of photos at 1 meter and 3 meters. There are other aspects of real stereo photography that we couldn't achieve, but the end result, crude as it was, allowed the scientist to calculate the size of objects where otherwise such calculation was nearly impossible.

The geologist was interested in photographing objects from 5 to 7 feet away, depending on the lighting and visibility. Our stereo modification, with a short focal distance, severely limited the quality of photographs taken. Joe Thompson rued the day that he had been shown by André how to shim up the lens of the camera into the stereo position. It seemed that as soon as he changed the camera for the biologists the next dive would be geological, requiring a change back to the original position. One could walk by the photo van and hear poor Joe mumbling curses to himself as he carefully performed the change-over. It took some time to make the lens modification, which increased in difficulty as the seas made up.

Our last week of diving in the year 1964 went smoothly. Dr. Shepard made an interesting dive down the head of Scripps Canyon, noting a sediment buildup there, which was more than he saw during his previous Saucer dives in February. He spurred Canoe on into so narrow a part of the canyon that they severely damaged the current meter and part of the fiberglas fairing by going under an overhanging cliff. Dr. Eric Barham of NEL followed by making some valuable first observations of the deep scattering layer (DSL), an acoustic reflecting layer of organisms that had long eluded oceanographers. The DSL had become well known to those who watched echo sounders on ships. Many a sleepy bridge-watch at night aboard a merchant vessel has been alarmed to see a solid bottom on the echo sounder record where deep water was supposed to be—and found to his relief it was only a false bottom or sound-scattering layer. Myriad small fish and invertebrates caused the echo sounder signal to reflect. The DSL was of military significance, since these layers fluctuated between night and day, strongly affecting sonar performance. The NEL scientists wished to learn more of the DSL, using the *Saucer* for direct observations for close-up identification. These observations were preparatory work for a series of dives Dr. Barham planned to make in Mexican waters.

At year's end we noted that we had made a total of 46 dives (including several training dives) in just less than two months. We had contracted for a minimum of 15 dives each month for a fixed price. Any dives beyond this number gave the company a bonus payment. To the scientist it meant that he was getting his dives at a lesser cost per dive, while our company made a little more than the original contract price. We felt that we had been able to accomplish most of the objectives set by the scientist and the engineer and that we had learned a lot in doing it. We had had no serious incidents or accidents and the overall system appeared to be as safe as possible.

Of the dives made thus far, one had been written up in the "sensation" column in the newspapers. Admittedly, there had been some tense moments. This particular dive had been our first night dive, made while we were aboard the *Hugh Tide.* Dr. E. W. Fager, a marine biologist at Scripps, wanted to observe the animals off La Jolla at night, in an attempt to correlate day and night activities of certain organisms. For this dive Fred Willett had purchased a high-intensity flashing light, to enable us to locate the *Saucer* when it came back. Dr. Fager had made other *Saucer* dives and knew the problems of photography and light backscatter in the water. He suggested a light off to the side, if possible, which would avoid the backscatter and make viewing easier. With the help of Gaston we rigged one of the 200-watt wing lights on a piece of angle iron bolted to the side of the front starboard wing. The dive was launched around eleven o'clock at night. We set a buoy for reference. Larry and I were in the tracking boat. We received occasional messages over the telephone that very few fish were being seen, and it was a dull dive for Dr. Fager. We drifted along overhead on an absolutely still sea. The *Saucer* was now coming up the slope gradually. Canoe announced that he had dropped the weight and that he was at about 130 meters. We waited a few minutes. Then a few more.

"He should be on the surface by now," said Larry, looking all around us for a sign of the flashing light.

"I still hear the pinger, don't you?" I asked.

"Yeah. That's funny. What are they doing?"

After a few minutes we heard the telephone.

"This is *Soucoupe, Soucoupe,*" came Canoe's calm voice. "We are caught. Looks like a rope or cable. Maybe it is the buoy line."

We reported the news to the *Hugh Tide.*

Next Dr. Fager said something about pulling on the buoy line. We started in that direction, not quite knowing what he meant or how the light anchor of the buoy line could hold down the *Saucer.* Canoe said they were at 80 meters.

We waited, wondering what it would be like to scuba dive to this depth. It would be nearly impossible, we thought, without double tanks, high-powered lights, or any other deep-diving back-up. Anyway, they would be all right for some 20 hours. While such wild ideas passed through our minds, there was a splash nearby. We saw the flashing light blinking, and there was the *Saucer.* It was riding strangely, with the stern sticking high out of the water. As the ship moved in and the crane plucked it out of the sea, I shone our spotlight up under the *Saucer* and saw that the emergency weight was gone. We scrambled aboard the *Hugh Tide* and crowded around to see what had happened. Between Canoe's account and Dr. Fager's report we put the story together. Apparently the *Saucer* had been slowly working its way up the slope and had come up beneath one of those many cables or ropes that Dr. Inman had reported seeing earlier. The cable had caught neatly in the light-bracket angle iron. Canoe had noticed when he dropped the ascent weight that they had moved for a while, then stopped. They came up about 60 meters, taking all the slack, and were finally caught. He had tried every possible way to maneuver out and was never really sure what it was that held them, because it was beyond the viewing angle of the port. He decided that he had to drop the 400-pound emergency weight, even though it meant a sharp tear-away and possibly integral damage to the vehicle. As it was, the angle iron bracket sheared with no damage to anything else. Father Neptune had claimed one light and 400 pounds of lead, but the *Saucer* and occupants arrived safely on the surface.

The *Saucer* proved that it had a dependable working emergency-ascent system, but we considered more carefully what type of protruding devices we would place on the vehicle in the future. In the Scripps–La Jolla area the canyons could be dangerous for the many things that could get fouled with the *Saucer* in the bottom or up the sides of the canyons.

After a later review of the incident we placed an additional 24-hour tank of breathing oxygen inside the *Saucer*. If the occupants were trapped, the extra tank would give additional time for a Navy rescue ship to reach the scene. Such additional time was especially important because we were going to be in remote parts of the Mexican coast. The Navy's McCann Bell could reach extreme depths of 800 feet for rescue. We also installed a magnetically controlled releasable safety float that would mark the *Saucer's* position.

The *Burch Tide* was scheduled to leave on January 2 and head south for the 800-mile trip to Cabo San Lucas in Baja California. During the last week of December, Scripps and NEL personnel and technicians had been bringing equipment aboard for the expedition. Now, on the evening of the 2nd, the loading activity stepped up to a furious pace. There was a steady procession of boxes of film, tape, sample containers, corers, a winch, and personal belongings coming aboard.

Bob Dill brought two of the famous Tote-Goat motor scooters and lashed them on deck. They had been used in Mexico before for exploring remote areas.

The *Deepstar* group had decided that since there were to be no dives on the trip down we would fly to San Lucas and meet the ship there. We felt we could better spend the extra hours with our families, whom we wouldn't see for nearly two months. The *Burch Tide* departed late that night on its three-day voyage.

On the 4th of January, a pleasantly warm morning, we headed for the airport across the border in Tijuana, 20 miles south of San Diego. We were joined by André, who had left us after San Clemente Island to go home for Christmas. He would assist us in piloting the *Saucer* during the numerous dives scheduled at San Lucas and the adjacent islands.

We stood around the small, noisy airport waiting for the immigration officials to stamp our visitor permits. All the official arrangements had been made by Dr. Dill and Dr. Carl Hubbs through the Mexican authorities, who granted the ship and crew permission to work in Mexican waters. Dr. Hubbs was a noted Scripps ichthyologist who was to make some dives later off La Jolla. As a courtesy, Dill and Hubbs had invited several interested Mexican scientists to visit our operation and perhaps make dives. For our purposes in traveling to meet the ship we now entered as "touristas" since we were expected to arrive as part of the ship.

Finally the line moved and we were admitted. After another short wait the aircraft, a DC-6, arrived from Los Angeles and we boarded, prepared for a flight of about two hours. Every seat was taken. The steward made a head-count as the plane was poised to taxi down the runway for takeoff. The steward looked perturbed. Apparently the passenger list and the number of heads didn't tally. Part way down the runway the pilot chopped the throttles and turned back toward the airport. There was mumbling and murmuring as passengers looked out and around. All inboard engines stopped. The boarding ramp was wheeled up to the forward entrance. Finally an elderly peasant woman carrying paper sacks made her way back from the flight deck. She had been forgotten. We were truly in a foreign country. The next time we took off without any untoward event.

I could see out to the east as we flew near the coast. The terrain was as rugged and hostile looking as any I recall. I kept expecting to see snow in the mountains, because they were so jagged and high. The water of the Gulf of California looked azure and delightful for diving. I hoped that Cabo San Lucas would be as inviting. I dozed off for a while. Soon we had banked over La Paz harbor and began our approach. The pattern for this airport sent us off on a long leg some 10 miles into the wilds. I could see the ground, which was nothing but cactus, mesquite, and scrub. The plane turned back toward the airport, flying only several hundred feet off the ground. Then it touched lightly down on the strip. La Paz airport was small but neat, with a large open patio. We had hardly collected ourselves when a young man with dark glasses asked us if we were going to San Lucas. He had a list of our names.

"Quickly," he said, "this way, please," gesturing to a boy to bring our luggage. "We must leave immediately, before it is too dark."

We had been expected by the air taxi operators who flew passengers going to the hotels south of La Paz. Apparently our plane had arrived late and since the rest of our journey was to be by small plane they wanted to get there before nightfall.

We walked down the flight line of beautiful, sleek twin-engined planes. Ours must be one of these, I thought. But no—we stopped beside a single-engine, high-wing, fabric-covered craft. The pilot said, "I'll take five of you, plus luggage."

I thought he was kidding—but as we moved on toward the plane I saw that there were six seats plus a large belly-luggage compartment. Larry, Joe, a stranger apparently bound for the same hotel, Val, and I all squeezed in—with some apprehension. Val had his private license and I could see him sizing up the plane and looking doubtful. Val tipped the scales at a good 250 pounds. I really wondered if the pilot knew what he was about. He spoke good *ingles* however and certainly wasted no time. The minute the pilot had packed in the last suitcase, he fired off the engine. It had a reassuring deep throb. He taxied along a short strip and then, with a quick tower clearance, we were at full throttle—no warm-up, run-up, or anything. The plane lifted off as though it were jet assisted and we were well above the runway in no time, banking into the sunset and heading south. The other single-engined white plane followed us closely. A third plane, carrying the remainder of our party, was a two-engine Cessna. It passed us soon and disappeared into the gathering twilight.

Below, I could see a fairly regular countryside. On the left were high mountains and to the right the Pacific Ocean, glistening with the last faint light. All the way from Tijuana no signs of habitation had been visible. Now we did glimpse an occasional group of ranch buildings. As the darkness rushed westward we began to see the twinkle of scattered fires. There was one road from La Paz and I could see the lights of a car moving slowly below. The plane hummed along, moving about in the air currents; it still seemed awfully light for six persons. The pilot began to talk on the radio, but it was hard to understand much of what he said. I guess my "Mexican" was rusty. I gathered he was conferring with our destination, whatever that was—the airport or hotel. We assumed the landing field would be small.

It was now totally dark. We could make out, faintly, some lights and large pinnacles of rock near what was probably water. The plane banked sharply and began its descent. Soon we saw lights ahead and some very faint flares along the edge of the field. Two car headlights shone on it momentarily. Our landing lights suddenly picked up the ground. The plane was a bit high. In a rapid sequence the pilot inexplicably pulled up his flaps, which set off his stall-warning buzzer; the plane began to fall like a rock. He gunned his engine, but it was too late. We dropped the last ten feet—straight down it seemed. We only bounced twice, bounding down the gravel strip like a jackrabbit. The pilot in halting English apologized for the bad landing. It was amazing that the plane with all that load did so well on the dirt and gravel runway. The other plane followed us in.

Fifteen minutes later we were riding in open trucks through the outskirts of the village. There were no street lights and occasionally we could catch a glimpse of a small house with a thatched roof and lit by a kerosene lantern.

The road was nothing but heavy sand and it was very dusty running through the occasional arroyos. Soon we climbed a steep hill over what was a beach ridge and arrived at the Hacienda. It was brightly lit and most elegant in appearance. We would stay here overnight or until the ship arrived. It had been a long day and we realized that we hadn't eaten. We joined the rest of the NEL and Scripps scientists in the dining room for dinner—it seemed like the middle of the night but it was only seven o'clock.

The hotel was owned by a man named Rodriguez, the son of the former Mexican president. Like the other two big hotels farther up the coast, this one catered to Americans, who were usually game fishermen or wealthy tourists interested in out-of-the-way places. The Hacienda had been built the year before, mostly from native materials. The cinder blocks were made there by a local handyman. The floors were beautifully tiled and the woodwork ornately carved and stained by local carpenters. There were rooms for 40 or 50 guests. At this moment there were perhaps ten other visitors besides us, for the season hadn't begun.

The food was good, plain, and not what I had expected in a place so far removed from any city. I had visions of wonderful exotic dishes and was disappointed when John Houchen from NEL explained:

"Nearly all the food is flown in from San Diego on the private plane. It's cheaper, they say, and they can get a better selection. And then it doesn't make people who aren't used to Mexican food get so upset at first. Wait till you taste the bread they make—that's as Mexican as you can get."

John was right, the bread was delicious. We had hot crisp rolls with local butter. Another local item was fresh fruit; the papayas were especially sweet and juicy. After dinner several of the gang started a card game, but I was tired and turned in early. Consequently I woke just after sunrise and had made a short tour of the grounds by seven o'clock when the dining room opened. It was a beautiful spot from which to look over the harbor and at the jagged sheer-faced rocks forming the peninsula and southernmost part of Baja California. The hotel was perched atop a beach ridge nearly 100 feet above the sea. At the head of the harbor, as well as the head of the San Lucas Canyon, stood the fish cannery. This is the principal industry in San Lucas and is government subsidized. The fish are taken from neighboring waters and there is usually one or more fishing vessels unloading at the long pier. At the height of the processing season from 200 to 300 people are employed there. The cannery is the heart of the village activity. It has the town's main electrical power generator, a pier with diesel fuel, fresh potable water, and a whistle that takes the place of a town-hall clock.

On the back side of the ridge was the village, lying in a depression surrounded by hills. Just behind the hotel was a short sand and gravel airstrip used for daytime landings of the hotel plane and other guests' airplanes. Beyond the airstrip lay a field of cactus and mesquite, and slightly above this arroyo was the village. I could see only a few buildings from the hotel. After a breakfast of *huevos con rancheros* (eggs scrambled with peppers) and papaya, with more of those home-made rolls, I was ready for a full day of activity.

After breakfast I met John Houchen, Dave Moore, Jerry Winterer, and Joe Curray. They were planning a geological field trip, and since I was a geologist several times removed I volunteered to join them.

The rest of the *Deepstar* boys slept on. We wanted to get an early start, so we left them to their slumber and walked to the village, where we waited for transportation at the one general store. The store was full of dry goods, groceries, dried vegetables and fruit, and various other strange-shaped things on the shelves. The owner was Chinese. He had been here since 1923 running the store, and now his son had taken over most of the work. We stood around drinking a *refresca* while John tried to find his friend Keith Ross to rent his truck. He returned shortly to say that Keith was not in town. Instead of Keith's truck, he hired a car to take us along the coastal road to San Jose del Cabo and back for the whole day at $14.00. At about nine o'clock the five of us were on our way in a Ford sedan, circa 1958. We drove down the main street in town past the *cantina*, which was the center of most social activity. Just on the edge of the village is a prosperous ranch that belongs to a Japanese farmer who raises all the vegetables for the town. His ranch was blessed with an excellent well and lots of water for crops. He and the Chinese shopkeeper were probably the wealthiest men in the village.

The road along the coast was a single lane with two deep ruts in the sandy gravel where one car traveled. Occasionally there were wide spots where two cars could pass. The surface varied from rough corrugated to stretches of bedrock, so the average speed was 20–25 miles per hour. The road wound in and out, up and down, along the coastal ridges. It crossed a wide arroyo where when it rained torrents of water rushed to the sea. We could see evidence of such activity. Near the beach we came on an interesting rock outcrop and Joe and Dave called for a halt to inspect it. They took some photographs where one layer of outcropping rock lay unconformably on top of another.

The town of San Jose del Cabo is about 40 kilometers from San Lucas, but the rough, winding roads made it seem farther. The town was appreciably larger than San Lucas and was the county seat. It, and the surrounding countryside, had a population of 11,000 inhabitants. As we came into the town we saw paved streets and street lights. We arrived at the town common or square about 11:30 AM, and told the driver we'd meet him in an hour. Joe and Dave were interested in buying liquor to take home to California. It was not sold in San Lucas. While they visited a local distillery, Jerry and I visited the primitive and ancient cathedral across from the plaza. On the front of the church was a mural depicting an attack on some early missionaries who had been killed by Indians in 1734. Inside we noted that it was a very poor church, with crude architecture. The building seemed to be of a much later date than the incident it commemorated. The town did, however, have a number of very old buildings, some, we learned, dating back to 1680. It had been one of the real centers of early civilization in Baja and had been mostly a fishing town but never a marine port, because there was no harbor or deep water. At present, however, it was more the agricultural center of the country.

We walked through the shopping district, but the stores had little of interest. They carried the cheapest cloth, blankets, tin ware, and essentials. I had hoped to find Indian and native goods, but there were none. The people bought only new, poor, machine-made goods.

I heard an intriguing story about the local inhabitants. Some people in the area of San Jose del Cabo were especially light-skinned and fair-haired for Mexicans. They sometimes had names like Smith, Jones, and other familiar American names. During the great gold rush of 1849 a stream of prospectors and adventurers had come from the east to California by ship around Cape Horn. On one such ship, a particularly mean and conniving captain had other business that he wished to pursue and, not wanting to beat to windward up the long coast of Baja, put the poor unsuspecting men and a few women ashore. He apparently convinced them in their ignorance that "over them hills lies San Francisco." This hardy clan is, according to the story, still settled back in the hills, although they assimilated with the native population, surviving partly as light-skinned and fair-haired people.

The next morning I again arose early and as I looked south toward the tip of the Cape, the *Burch Tide* came around right on schedule. Our vacation was over. Now back to work.

Our schedule called for two weeks in and around Cabo San Lucas. Then on to the Tres Marías Islands in Costa de Nayarit, which lay 300 to 400 miles to the southeast.

While the ship went through Mexican customs, declarations, and inspection we began to collect our gear to move aboard. The *Burch Tide* had docked at the cannery pier so that supplies could be easily loaded. The harbor was crystal clear around the pier and full of fish. Even here, where they dumped waste from the cannery, the water had excellent visibility. The head of the canyon began off the end of the pier at a depth of 100 feet and descended steeply as it proceeded out of the harbor close to the nearly vertical walls of the cliffs. The *Saucer*'s limit of 1,000 feet was reached less than a mile from the cannery.

By afternoon we had moved aboard all hand luggage and the variety of gear sent by the scientists, who would continue to live ashore at the Hacienda. The first dive was to be made about two hours' run from San Lucas, so we decided to wait until the next day, which was Thursday, January 7.

The ship arrived at Gorda Bank around nine in the morning. Dr. Joseph Curray, a Scripps marine geologist, was interested in the pinnacle of the bank, which rises up to within 8 fathoms of the surface, about 5 miles offshore. To obtain the several profiles he wanted of the surrounding area, the ship made a number of passes using the survey depth sounder that NEL had newly installed aboard. This was a precision depth recorder (PDR) and the latest in electronics. It could give the oceanographer a very accurate profile of the bottom. By the time we had set our buoy marker on the edge of the bank and were ready to launch the *Saucer* it was noon.

Those who were less familiar with our operation often wondered why we said the hours on this job were long when a dive itself was "only four hours." The time involved in reaching the site, surveying it, and delays in getting the *Saucer* launched really all added up to many more hours than four. Moreover, the pre-survey for a dive was most important to the geological scientists so that they would not overlook any significant features or perhaps waste a whole dive. We appreciated the need to make a complete search for the right diving location. Of course, in local or "home" water the scientists would usually survey the area beforehand and avoid using our ship's time for this purpose.

Joe Curray explained to Canoe that he wanted to start the dive part of the way down the gentle slope and inspect the area where it dropped off into rougher terrain. He wanted to see the nature of the change from sand to silt on the steeper slope and then proceed to the outcrop of the sedimentary rocks. We launched the *Saucer* in a fairly calm sea where the depth was 105 meters. Joe Thompson and André couldn't resist the clear water and decided to make a dive part way with the *Saucer*. We had done very little scuba work so far—only at San Clemente. We had decided earlier that our divers should be limited to 175 feet, unless a recompression chamber was on board. The *Saucer* was cut loose and Joe and André were already on their way down to keep up with the *Saucer's* descent. In *Shazam* Jerry and I watched their column of bubbles. After about five minutes I figured they should be on their way back. Finally, after seven or eight minutes, we could see them clearly still coming up at 30 or 40 feet below. When they surfaced, Joe checked his See-view pressure gauge. He was always proud of the small amount of air he used. It read 1,400 pounds. Then André read his and it was only 1,300. This meant they had used less than half their tanks. I was sure these two must be doing something fantastic to conserve air.

"How far down did you go with the *Saucer*?" I asked Joe.

He grinned and said, "Well, my depth gauge said around 180 feet, if I read it right. But when I looked at André's it was at 225 feet. I think mine's not working right."

I could see this upset Larry, who tried to keep us following our rules. His experience in the Navy had been quite different from that of civilian divers. Joe always enjoyed deep diving and having had a lot of experience, handled himself well.

After we returned the divers to the *Burch Tide* we went back to track the *Saucer* off to the southwest. The saucernauts reported once that all they were seeing was flat sandy bottom. They traversed this area for perhaps an hour when they finally reached a gradual increase in slope at 175 meters. At this point the *Saucer* stopped moving. We drifted slowly over the spot where they were. Then the telephone gave its characteristic squeak as the *Saucer* microphone was keyed. I turned up the volume.

"*Shazam, Shazam.* Here is the *Soucoupe.*"

We moved slightly to the north to get directly over them and receive the strongest signal.

"*Soucoupe, Soucoupe.* Go ahead."

"We have difficulty with the propulsion motor. Cannot keep it running. Have tried everything, but it's now stopped completely. We are returning."

What now, we wondered? It was too bad to spoil a dive when the scientist had just reached the site he wanted to work in. If we could fix the motor, we would have liked to give him another dive, but the rules of the contract had been established by Fred Spiess and Tom Horton, who had chosen an hour as the minimum requisite length of a dive based on their experience with the first dives in *Saucer* '64. If the *Saucer* was able to stay down an hour, it meant that everything was probably working properly. On the other hand, if there were problems, they seemed to occur well before an hour was up.

Gaston found the trouble was in the motor switch for the water pump. Soon after, he told Fred the *Saucer* was now ready again. Fred thought we ought to have time to get in a training dive since there wouldn't be another one for the customer. He came by the office van where I was interviewing Joe Curray and said I would probably have a chance to make a quick dive. I was slightly distracted as I listened to Joe relate what he'd seen, for like the rest of the team, I had been looking forward to a dive after being so close to the *Saucer* for several months. The *Saucer* had not gone as far as Joe wanted, and he had traveled over a lot of gently sloping sand bottom. The steep break in the slope lay farther on.

While we talked, a very loud and ominous banging started somewhere in the ship, as though someone was striking it with a huge hammer. There was a bit of commotion on deck and the ship came to "all stop." By the time I got out on deck Larry was saying something about the propeller hitting the ship. I wondered what we could have hit or fouled in the propeller. Ken went over the side to inspect it. It didn't take him long to see that our starboard propeller shaft was broken. The short end with the propeller had slipped back in the tube and now rested against the rudder. When we moved through the water it turned, beating the rudder unmercifully. Larry and Ken took overboard a large section of cable given them by the engineer, Gene, which they lashed to the prop to keep it from thrashing and then secured the end to the bit on deck.

With this fixed, we proceeded toward San Lucas under power from the port bank of engines, making only a bare six knots. It wasn't until we were discussing the accident with Earl and Fred that I realized what this meant to the diving schedule. We thought at first that we could probably make our dives in San Lucas since all of them were to take place in the harbor. Earl pointed out that with only one screw the ship had no maneuverability at all. We couldn't make our usual approach, which was to head on to the *Saucer*, then turn the ship stern to and back up to it. Further, although it would be possible to back and fill and eventually get in position, if there were any kind of emergency that required fast retrieval, we would be badly handicapped.

In the best interest of the program it was apparent that we had to get the ship to a shipyard as soon as possible. The nearest yard that could haul the *Burch Tide* was on the mainland at Mazatlán. We reached port late that evening and the Scripps group decided that since this repair would take at least five days it would be wise for them to return to San Diego.

Our contract had not taken into consideration the possibility of a ship breakdown; we were therefore still obligated to make the required minimum of 15 dives this month. If all went as planned, we could possibly keep to our schedule provided we got out of the shipyard by the 17th.

We bade our friends good-bye and took a hasty departure the next evening for Mazatlán although the skipper had heard that the weather was not favorable out in the Gulf. By dark we could see the sea was getting rough, so Fred asked us to secure all equipment on the afterdeck. Ken Lange lashed *Shazam* down with a heavy line and Jerry and I proceeded to make fast the other loose items. Gasoline drums for the outboard were lashed, as well as oil drums and oxygen tanks. Already water was beginning to slosh about on deck as the *Burch Tide* rolled easily, taking seas through the scuppers and washing back over the stern. When we were squared away we all retired to the large van to see a movie. Joe Thompson had managed to rent a number of old 16mm sound films that were usually shown on the San Diego tuna fleet. The *Burch Tide* continued to roll more heavily now and before we got to the second reel of a typical western, the screen fell over several times. The movie had to be postponed. Several of us went to the wheelhouse to watch the sea. It had become markedly rougher in the last hour. We had begun to come out from under the lee of the land into the Gulf, where the wind seemed to be blowing a whole gale. I turned in around 10 PM and looked out the window of the van to see water at least a foot deep pour down the deck between the vans.

Although we rolled only 15 or 20 degrees, this was a lot for this flat-bottomed barge of a ship and she felt strange as she lurched in the troughs of the waves. I wondered how securely the vans had been welded down to the deck. The ship plowed on, laboring under half power and probably making only 4 to 5 knots. We had come 45 miles and were fully out in the Gulf. With 145 miles to go to Mazatlán, it would take a long time to get there.

I got up to watch the sea again. From the wheelhouse, looking aft, I could see that the waves were steep, perhaps 10 to 12 feet high. Sometimes one would break on the side of the vans as we ran through the trough. The skipper estimated that wind was gusting to 50 knots. Finally he decided that since we had only half power and that if anything happened to the port engines we would be in trouble, it would be best to turn back. Soon after, we re-entered the lee of the shore and we all slept a little better. We were back in San Lucas by daybreak.

We spent more pleasant days in Cabo San Lucas while the wintry winds lashed the Gulf of California. Earl told us that he had visited a Mexican shrimp boat nearby that also wanted to get to Mazatlán. The skipper of that boat had heard reports of 90-mile-an-hour winds blowing in the Gulf. Safe in the harbor, we could scarcely believe it, for the weather was lovely and mild.

During our days of "forced vacation," when most of us were swimming or sailing, Gaston was hard at work on his movie camera. Earlier he had been concerned about the speed of the drive mechanism and had it all apart. Now, he thought that the sighting frame wasn't showing the exact picture he was photographing. The camera was an elderly Bell & Howell turret type that he had purchased on his first trip to the United States. It seemed to be more of a nuisance than an asset. Gaston set up an elaborate procedure to measure the scene seen by each of the turret lenses and aimed the camera on a tripod at the wheelhouse. He sketched each view accurately and precisely to try to reduce the results in some way. The entire effort became far too involved and complicated for me—or for what I thought the camera was worth. Gaston was the embodiment of precision and perfection, but I don't know that he improved the camera. More likely he became all the more aware of its faults.

Fred believed it would be safe enough to get in a couple of training dives for Joe and Larry in shallow water near the edge of the San Lucas Canyon and toward the east part of the harbor. Here the *Burch Tide* could lay to and maneuver more easily than close to the rocky shore. These were advanced dives for both pilot trainees, giving them the chance to "fly the *Saucer*" over rough bottom and take some photographs of the steep walls of the canyon.

The trip to Mazatlán was pleasant and the sea much calmer than we had expected after the blow. It didn't seem possible that it was the same body of water. During the thirty hours for transit we sunbathed, wrote letters home, or did general maintenance work to the ship.

The entrance to Mazatlán harbor is guarded on one side by a large rock rising 300 feet from the water and covered by a thin vegetation of mesquite. The channel is narrow and long, with a breakwater to the south. The city lies 3 or 4 miles from the entrance, on low land that gives way to foothills and rugged low mountains 20 or 30 miles distant. As we approached the series of long wharves I could see what a busy and large commercial port it was. Everywhere there were numerous shipyards engaged in ship- and boat-building. We found that all the wharves were already full or scheduled for ships coming to unload, so we anchored out in the edge of the channel several hundred yards offshore. We had to press *Shazam* into service as a personnel boat, and after supper that evening the liberty party was ferried ashore in several trips.

We met Fred and Earl at one of the larger hotels down along the beach waterfront. They had just finished calling our Baltimore office to report on the schedule for repairing the ship. The propeller shaft for the *Burch Tide* to replace the broken one had been shipped from New Orleans by truck to the border and from there by rail. It would be at the shipyard by the weekend. Charlie Jenkins, our boss in Baltimore, took the opportunity of this long interruption in our operation to recall Fred and me to discuss plans for the rest of the program and to bring him up to date on our progress so far. We were to fly back the next day. I was glad of the chance to return East for a while but regretted that I would miss spending some time in Mazatlán. However, I was up early the next morning and ashore again to do some shopping at the large city market typical of those in most Mexican towns and cities. There was booth after booth of pottery, textiles, brooms, baskets, and the rare and strange-looking dried foods. The cloth and leather were of good quality, well made, and nearly unobtainable in border towns, where only junk abounded. I found some sandals I had been looking for—the kind I'd seen people wearing in San Lucas but couldn't find for sale there. They had leather upper soles and rubber bottom ones made from an old automobile tire. They were perfect for use on the ship's deck, because most of the time it was wet or even slightly awash. I saw several handmade wooden spoons, brushes, and useful but craftsy type things that cost all together less than a dollar. I bought two additional pairs of sandals for $2.20. Not so bad, as Gaston would say. I walked quickly through the main part of the market looking at the meat hanging at the butcher shops and the heaps of produce, and smelling the strange mixture of spices, baskets, leather, and people. The fruit looked especially tempting. On my way back to the ship I passed one of the numerous sidewalk vendor's wagons. He had a great stack of fresh pineapple. I stood in line and watched the young woman ahead of me sprinkling a slice of pineapple with what looked like cinnamon sugar. I tried the same.

"Lo mismo," I ventured to the man in his white apron. "Y combien?"

"Si, señor, es cuarenta centavos," he responded. "Y es muy bueno!"

I walked on down the street feeling very smug, as if I were an old hand at all this. I bit expectantly into the large slice on which I'd poured much cinnamon. Only it wasn't cinnamon—it was the hottest peppers I'd ever tasted. I should have known better—the Mexicans would always be hot rather than sweet.

Fred and I left for Baltimore that afternoon. I was to stay East for about ten days and then rejoin the ship when it came back to Cabo San Lucas.

It was decided to try to make all the originally planned dives both at the Costa de Nayarit and at Cabo San Lucas by moving the program schedule of the next major customer, the Navy Underwater Sound Laboratory. There was still a month of diving remaining in Mexico. Depending on the repairs, the ship would leave the following Monday for Nayarit and make some dives for Joe Curray. As our plane circled out over the harbor and I caught a brief glimpse of the ship at anchor and then the view westward over the Pacific, and as we flew southward, I guessed that those low islands near the horizon might possibly be the Tres Marías, where the team would be in a week.

Upon arrival in Baltimore I found that as consolation for missing the next leg of the *Saucer* journey I was to spend four or five days in Puerto Rico and St. Croix. It was thought that this area might be a good test site for *Deepstar* DS-4000 and her sea trials and I was to inspect it for possible facilities.

Project Diving Saucer '65 was now halfway through its

allotted time. We realized we had to press on if we were to fulfill the requirements of our contract and, more important, if we were to satisfy our individual customers and thus demonstrate that the diving business was in fact practicable and profitable. We had already accomplished more in the number of dives, diversity of operation, and geographic span than any group we knew of to date. However, this was no time to slow down, but rather a time to try to improve.

CHAPTER 8

Cabo San Lucas
Revisited

I sat on the steps leading from the terrace to the beach in front of the Hacienda, basking in the warm noon sun. I had been sitting for half an hour talking with Dr. and Mrs. Shepard as we waited for the arrival of the *Burch Tide* that afternoon. The Shepards had flown in the day before and, along with Bob Dill and John Houchen, were staying at the hotel. We were looking forward to diving in the *Saucer* in the canyon that lay beneath the harbor waters before us. Finally we could see a small object far at sea. Gradually it became large enough for us to identify the orange crane on the stern and the characteristic hull of the *Burch Tide*.

We wondered how the dives in Nayarit had gone and if all was in readiness for the next series for Drs. Shepard, Dill, and Salas. I gathered they had tried several times to call by radio to the *Burch Tide* but had been unable to raise her. Communications on the surface had been far from ideal after the ship left California. The ship-to-shore marine-operator frequency from Los Angeles, KOU, was usually weak, although we had had some success using it in Mazatlán at night. Our radio on board was unable to raise the high-seas operator in San Francisco, KMI; so we used a larger set on one of the local yachts so we could easily make contact except when atmospherics interfered. Just before we had left San Diego, a special frequency allocated to Scripps had been installed on the *Burch Tide*, but the antenna had never been properly tuned, so we had no use of it. This radio frequency was used by Scripps oceanographic vessels all over the Pacific. The one frequency that was normally an emergency channel at home on which we might have been able to communicate ship to ship was crowded with Mexican fishermen and entirely too noisy. The only thing we could be fairly sure of was the citizens band radios that we all carried when going ashore or on excursions near by. We could talk up to a distance of several miles or more from the ship to *Shazam* or to any of the many portable sets.

The *Burch Tide* plowed her way into the outer part of the harbor, resembling one of the Great Lakes ore boats pushing a wall of water in front of her, "bone in her teeth," coming straight at us. As she changed course slightly I could see that the *Saucer* was still on the stern in one piece. The *Burch Tide* slowed down, moved slowly into shallow water and good holding ground, and let her starboard anchor go with a rattle loud enough to echo off the high rocks across the way. It was a beautiful day, without a cloud to be seen. I'm sure the humidity was below 30. High over the rocks of the peninsula were endless soaring frigate birds and an occasional buzzard riding the warm air updrafts.

John, Bob, Dr. Shepard, and I went out in the NEL "whaler," which we had borrowed from the *Trieste* group at

NEL. It had been brought down as a second boat for personnel use when *Shazam* was on tracking duty. After a busy summer with the *Trieste* engaged off Boston in the *Thresher* search, it showed its age and long service.

We boarded the *Burch Tide* amid cheers, hellos, and welcomes. Larry met me at the stern.

"How'd the dives go over at Nayarit and did you get all five?" I asked.

"Swell. It couldn't have been much better. The weather was perfect and calm. The *Saucer* worked fine—except for some minor difficulties with the instruments—and Dr. Curray made some dives that gave him a lot to look at and photograph."

"Did you tape the interviews and write them up?" I asked. I hoped he had, for I had enjoyed my vacation from transcribing these interviews into reports for the home office.

"Golly," said Larry with a long sigh, "I never realized what a job it is listening to all those comments and then trying to put them together into something that makes sense. I hope I don't have to do that again. Actually, it was interesting and I got a lot out of it."

I was pleased to hear that the process that had usually involved my efforts had operated without me. Maybe I could stay away longer next time.

"Fred says we're going to try to make a dive for Dr. Dill today," Jerry announced.

I moved up the deck feeling like a tourist and a stranger. All the crew was in shorts and at-sea clothes and here I was still in street clothes. When we had arrived in Mexico we had decided to shed our company uniforms in favor of shorts or bathing trunks. Because of the warmer water the pilots too had to wear less warm clothing. Canoe wore the light-cotton gray flight coveralls. Ken Lange was barely recognizable, he got so tanned in the week and half I'd been away. I hastily changed into shorts as we prepared to put the *Saucer* into the canyon. Joe Curray and party were all packed and ready to go ashore to get their plane home. I planned to read the reports that Larry had written up that evening.

The *Burch Tide* weighed anchor, swung around, and backed over toward the canyon area. While Dr. Shepard plotted the exact position where he and Bob had decided the dive should start, Ken was running over the *Saucer's* pre-dive check list. André and Bob were inside the *Saucer* and Gaston was talking with André on the sound-powered telephone. He looked over to Fred and nodded, saying his usual, "Read-ee."

Fred in turn gave the crane operator, Val this time, thumbs up and the *Saucer* eased out of the deck cradle. With the crane installation we had, it was necessary to top the crane boom all the way to the stop in order for the bottom of the *Saucer* to clear the 18-inch rail. Val next brought the tip of the lower arm back. Finally he would swing the crane to the right and out over the water to a position directly astern, then hold. If the ship had drifted or if the position wasn't exactly what we wanted, Earl would move the stern over. Dr. Shepard stepped out on the bridge wing and made two quick checks with his sextant, then stepped back inside to plot again. Next we heard the P.A. system.

"It's OK right here," said Earl in his Texas drawl. "Doc Shepard says this is the place."

Fred gave Val the down sign and the *Saucer* plopped beneath the rippled surface with just the hatch awash. The visibility looked excellent. Bob had told me earlier that he had known it to vary drastically from a fantastic 200 feet to barely 10 feet—all in a short time. So far our experience with visibility had been good, with upwards of 60 to 100 feet horizontally. Now Gaston had checked everything with André and had given the parting "*Ciaia.*" The phone wire and tag lines were disconnected and the *Saucer* settled down toward the bottom in 20 meters. We could actually see it from the deck of the *Burch Tide.* A group of NEL and *Deepstar* divers were ready to go over the side and departed one by one with several cumbersome-looking cameras. The *Saucer* rested on the bottom as the photo team got some good footage in shallow well-lighted water. So far we had been unable to photograph the *Saucer* against a reflecting light-colored background. The area around the edges of the canyon appeared excellent, because there was sand.

Since I'd been off on a jaunt while everyone else was working, I thought it only right to volunteer to man the tracking boat. There was little opposition. Tracking could be very dull at times, so we rotated the duty of diver and tracking-boat operator. John Houchen came along to transcribe notes and messages as Bob passed them up on the telephone. Unlike some of the scientists who had no use for the phone, Bob used it to report many observations. He also had John make routine checks in case he himself became too busy and forgot to report the observations of temperature, depth, course heading, etc. I found it helped us follow the *Saucer* and it also kept us busy on the surface. Many times *Shazam* duty meant taking sextant angles during the whole dive to be plotted in later. If there was accurate control and places to "shoot" at, it was easier and more exact to do this from the small boat instead of the *Burch Tide*.

"*Shazam . . . Soucoupe.*"

"Go ahead, *Soucoupe,*" we returned. The telephone was clear and sharp. It seemed as though it was finally operating correctly.

"We're proceeding down canyon. Slopes are steep—from 30 to 75 degrees with sand platforms. Depth 150 meters. Over."

"Roger that."

Every five to ten minutes Bob called in. The *Saucer's* progress into deep water was rapid.

"*Shazam . . . Soucoupe.* The bottom is full of small mounds and no ripple marks. Slope is maybe 10 degrees in the canyon axis. Over."

We acknowledged and continued to move slowly along the shore, which, in the afternoon shadow of the rocks, was now towering several hundred feet above us.

"*Shazam . . . Soucoupe,*" came the slightly watery voice. "The slope has changed to 30 degrees and the bottom is covered with granite rubble. Depth 270 meters. We see some ripple marks ahead and the current is about 0.2 knots. Over."

"Roger, *Soucoupe.* Read you loud and clear," said John.

The dive proceeded until the participants reached 300 meters, the maximum depth of the *Saucer*. Here they worked their way up the side of the canyon near Shepard Rock—a narrow pinnacle 50 feet offshore. This was an area of sand-fall activity. When sufficient amounts of sand moved down the beach slope above and exceeded the angle of repose—some 35 degrees—it started to flow like a river down into the canyon. I remembered seeing a movie made by Ron Church that showed these "rivers of sand" Bob Dill and others had studied on other San Lucas expeditions. Now it seemed that the sand was not flowing naturally. Bob asked us over the telephone to have the NEL divers start the sand moving in shallow water. In the *Saucer* he watched at a point where the sand should come spilling past down a chute at 85 meters. Finally a thin trickle of fine sand came over the rock edge and down the wall. The trickle lasted several minutes, then stopped. Bob concluded that it would take much more sand to make the "rivers" flow as he had seen them at other times. The dive was concluded around 4:30 PM. As Bob explained in his debriefing session, his purpose had been to continue the inspection of the granite canyon at depths below those he had reached as a scuba diver on earlier expeditions; he wanted to compare the sedimentary processes in this canyon with those he knew in the California canyons, such as Scripps and La Jolla.

That evening, after supper, Joe Thompson broke out another of the twenty or so movies we had and we congregated on deck to watch it. The weather at San Lucas couldn't have been better for outdoor movies—just cool enough at night but not chilly. Between reels Little Joe made buttered popcorn that we passed around. The movie was hilariously bad—pirates and sailing vessels—and the comments of Gaston and André were far more entertaining.

Later on I listened through some of the interview tapes of Joe Curray's dives off the Tres Marias Islands. Joe had studied this area before, from a surface ship, using an echo sounder and bottom-sediment profiler. He had wanted to find the old shore line and beach zone, now well submerged, and discover if any deposition or erosion was going on in the areas above and below this zone. He saw the old beach and shells of the intertidal zone at about 110 meters. This beach was believed to be about 18,000 years old. The *Saucer* had picked up two samples here that Joe could retrieve for later analysis. Some 135 meters below this area the divers encountered a different type of bottom, which represented the area that had been below sea level and probably submerged for at least 50,000 years, placing it in Pleistocene time in the geological calendar. They also saw a number of flatfish, shrimp, a few crabs, and many shell fragments. Above the beach zone Joe had noted the unbelievable density of Galatea crabs swarming over the bottom and in the water column. These crabs had been stirring up the bottom and kept it in constant motion.

Larry related an episode that I wished I could have experienced. As the *Burch Tide* moved from one of the islands to a new dive site she ran into a severe storm. Earl looked at the chart and noted that they might avoid the wind and seas if they could get in a lee. The largest island looked perfect, except that Earl could see some sort of warning boundary stated on the chart. They made for the shelter regardless, in the growing dark. The island was ideal, with high steep cliffs, deep water—a fine spot to ride out the night. The crew relaxed to watch a movie as the wind howled in the hills, until the chug-chug of a motorboat and some large spotlights intruded. Two armed guards came alongside in the boat and spoke harshly to Earl in "Mexican." Didn't he know it was forbidden to anchor here? The island was a penal colony and *Burch Tide* must leave at once. Protests were futile. No one was welcome there—not even *scientificos*. The *Burch Tide* crew reluctantly upped anchor and spent the night drifting and uncomfortable.

The next day they moved to the south of the island to make the film test dive. Joe Thompson and André went down in the *Saucer*. They had been on the bottom a short while when a radio message demanded that the *Burch Tide* depart immediately—the ship must be no less than 2 miles offshore. Fred radioed to Larry to contact the *Saucer* and get it up. They had visions of the gunboat coming out again while the *Saucer* was still diving. Shortly thereafter the *Saucer* surfaced, was recovered, and *Burch Tide* retreated quickly. This island of the Marías was not for science.

Describing another dive, Curray told of seeing several large green turtles busily feeding on the bottom. As the *Saucer* moved up to them they would swim away, but one or two came back to the bottom to feed on the shrimp where the saucernauts could watch. The depth was 180 meters. The turtles must have had tremendous endurance, since they must return to the surface for air.

I went to bed that evening full of thoughts of diving and the *Saucer*. It was good to be back aboard, amid all the activity and in one of the most exclusive tourist resort areas in Mexico. It would be impossible, I thought to myself, to convince anyone back in the office that this was work or could be difficult, exasperating, or downright unpleasant at times. At the moment, everything appeared to have been smoothed out in the operation itself. Yet we were not satisfied with one of our most important end products for the scientists; the photographs taken on the dives still were not as good as we knew they could be. Now that we were so far from the color laboratories in Hollywood where the films were developed it took even longer to get return information vital to the quality of the final picture. We suspected that the strobe light did not always flash at full intensity. Further, there was doubt that we were using the correct film emulsion. Since there were a variety of different environmental conditions that called for both different film and possibly a different way to process, there were many chances of spoiling the film. One of the dives off Nayarit had been made to evaluate various types of movie film under uniform conditions. André had conducted this experiment and now we were waiting for the results, but we all doubted that they would prove much. Sometimes it seemed that it might have been personal preference that affected the choice of film and subsequent endorsement of one type of emulsion. With such controversies spinning about in my mind I drifted off to sleep.

I was awakened by the strange cry of the gull of Baja California. It resembled a tern more than a gull but was neither as I knew them. The day promised to be another absolutely clear one, with the distant hills sharply outlined by the rising sun's light. The ubiquitous pelican was at work fishing and paddling about over toward the cannery. These ungainly birds soar none too easily and when they spot a fish they plummet to the water to capture a mouthful and then gulp it down. Great flocks of them gathered on the low rocks over against the cliffs and stared with large unblinking eyes, becoming frightened only when we got very close.

This morning our *Saucer* scientist was to be Dr. Francis Shepard of Scripps. He is one of the best known and respected marine geologists in the world and perhaps could be called *the* expert on submarine canyons. His objective, as Bob Dill's had been, was to compare this canyon with the others he knew and had explored by *Saucer*. He wanted to see how much evidence of erosion there was in the canyon.

For many years Dr. Shepard and many other leading marine geologists had sought an explanation for the submarine canyons and their formation. At first, when only a few canyons were known, he had speculated that they might be the result of a vast lowering of sea level during the glacial periods, when rivers could erode them above sea level. But this theory had to be rejected in the face of later evidence that sea level could not have been several thousand feet lower. The Dutch geologist, Kuenen, proposed a modified turbidity current, a dense cloud of suspended sediment which might initiate erosive action. The natural occurrence of such currents was rare and the initiating force difficult to explain. Various investigations by many scientific workers in the 1950's and early 1960's offered several explanations, yet came up with no convincing solutions that could explain all of the canyons. Bob Dill had done considerable research as part of his doctoral dissertation that indicated erosion at the heads of the canyons by sediment slumping and creeping.

Dr. Shepard, a vigorous man in his mid-sixties, set off in the small yellow *Saucer*. The dive went well. Bob Dill and Dr. Bill Salas, our visiting Mexican geologist, spent the morning in

Shazam following the course of Dr. Shepard as he and Canoe picked their way down the narrow granite canyon.

On his return after a full four-hour dive, we gathered in the office to hear about it. Dr. Shepard was impressed with the narrowness of the tributary where they had started and by the fact that there was no sediment on the bottom, which was only several meters wide. There were no ripple marks indicating current activity until they reached 270 meters in the main canyon, where Dill had seen marks the day before.

In San Lucas Canyon there were few, if any, of the overhanging cliffs that were so typical of Scripps Canyon. Further, the angle of the canyon walls ranged from 60 to 80 degrees but rarely approached the vertical walls of Scripps Canyon.

As they proceeded down the canyon it became broader. The first thing Dr. Shepard saw of real interest was a series of medium-sized granite blocks. He described them as having "remarkably fresh-looking surfaces—just as if you'd broken the granite off with a hammer. You could see the fresh granite with all the crystals showing in it."

"I suspect that these tumbled down from the edge of the steep cliffs nearby as part of an avalanche," added Bob Dill. "Yesterday we could see several blocks 5 or 6 feet across balanced on the edge of the canyon ready to fall over at any moment."

"Coming up the north wall," continued Dr. Shepard, "I don't recall seeing any fresh fractures, as I did in La Jolla Canyon."

"Did you see the current indications around those blocks?" asked Bob.

"Oh, yes, certainly very much of a tunneling effect at the corners. But I think there hasn't been any activity lately, because there's a fine cover of silt in the troughs of the current ripples."

"You commented on the phone that the visibility wasn't good," Bob reminded Dr. Shepard from his notes.

"Yes, it was maybe 20 feet at best. Most of the time there was a fine sediment—perhaps a mica—in the turbid water slowly moving down the canyon. The visibility improved below 230 meters where there was no sign of these currents. Actually there was no measurable current, although once I thought I saw a slight motion of the *Saucer* drifting along."

Toward the end of the dive the saucernauts inspected the now vertical walls for scour marks, but found none. In some spots it almost looked as though the walls were polished, but over all there was a thin cover of growth, concealing all detail.

Toward the end of the dive they saw a large hole in the side of the canyon at 184 meters. It was about 2 meters across and Dr. Shepard could see into it to a sand chute. They moved all around it, inspecting it and wondering where it led. It was a little too small to admit the *Saucer;* Dr. Shepard said he would have "objected strenuously to going into it!" They moved across to the north wall, a distance of some 75 meters, then back to the south wall, and finally up to the surface.

We wound up the dive 287 interview. The dives were going well. All the supplementary gear was now functioning perfectly. Our luck was almost too good. The *Saucer* batteries were put on charge, to enable us to dive again the following day. The rest of the day was ours to use.

A group was getting scuba gear together, charging bottles, and laying out equipment. By 1:30 in the afternoon André, Canoe, Joe, and Gaston decided to go fishing for our dinner. Ken, Larry, and I decided we wanted to explore the beach that separated the peninsula from the extreme point, known as "Land's End." The divers dropped us off.

The beach was usually called the Tombolo—after its geological name. A tombolo is a beach that joins an island with the mainland and is sometimes overwashed by the sea. We landed on the beach front, which was quite steep and led down to a tributary that entered the canyon. The top of the joining strip was probably 8 or 10 feet above sea level. The whole beach was perhaps 150 feet long between nearly sheer cliffs on both ends. It was littered with pelican bones, recent skeletons; several pelicans were lying in various states of ill health over toward the rocks. Overhead the buzzards and the frigate birds circled. One pelican looked as though he wanted to get to the water but couldn't. We picked him up and carried him down to it, but he was unable to navigate—so we placed him back on the sand. Another was in need of repair and had probably been in a fight. They all appeared to be sitting peaceably awaiting the end—perfectly calm and resigned. We couldn't resist renaming the beach. It was no longer Tombolo Beach, but "Dying Pelican Beach"—the graveyard for San Lucas pelicans.

We trudged off in the sand toward the ocean on the other side, 300 or 400 yards away. I tried to imagine the strength of the storm that could overwash this distance, as it must. The waves would then carry great volumes of sand over the narrow ridge and down into the canyon where the sand flows had been photographed earlier. The Pacific was relatively calm this day, with waves of 1 to 2 feet breaking on the steep beach. We walked around the water's end toward an enormous rock outcrop up the beach. There were some low rocks and ledges, with fascinating little tidal pools full of seaweed, snails, and other beasties that live happily there in the intertidal zone. Below us the waves sloshed and broke on the rocks, as they had for millions of years. We climbed up the slope face in curiosity and then, reaching the other side, crawled carefully around in bare feet along the sharp granite ledges. Finally we got around this big rock and back onto the beach. As far as we could see in any direction it was open, uninhabited, and unspoiled.

The sun, which was warm at first, had become hot. We went for a swim. The water was excellent. Soon it occurred to us that we could swim around the rock on our way back. So we struck off. I had become so used to diving and using flippers that normal swimming seemed difficult and it seemed as though I was making no progress. I kicked and kicked and barely seemed to move. As we moved slowly in front of the great rock the distance seemed far longer than it actually was. Finally we coasted in through the surf. I was clearly in need of more swimming exercise, but then I noticed that my UDT and EOD friends were also puffing a little.

We combed the beach on the way home and I found

numerous bits of smooth dirftwood—the kind tourists pay money for. I found so many that I had to discard some in favor of other, better pieces. When we arrived at Dying Pelican Beach we had to sit for a while waiting for the diving boat and looking at the sad pelicans. *Shazam* finally nosed around the rocks on its return, laden with a large catch of several kinds of fish, some lobster, and other goodies. I could taste them already.

Later, as it began to grow dark around 5:30, Little Joe stoked up the large charcoal grill he had for such occasions and put it in the aisle between the vans. When the coals were ready cooks Laban and Kientzy stepped forward with the fish and lobster they had caught by trolling and scuba, and began to cook them. André also passed out to any takers delicate parts of some of the shellfish he had gathered. I tried them again and found them far more palatable than the mussels from San Clemente. When the first fish and lobster were ready there was a line of hungry customers. The fish were a mixture of Sierra, Pes Fuerte, and other local species. Little Joe had thrown in some potatoes to bake and, if anyone should want them, a couple of steaks from the freezer. We filled our plates, then walked to the table in the ward room. Our dinner meal was always served with wine, which pleased the French. Fred had decided that this custom was essential for the morale of the troops—just like the ration of rum for sailors. We had our own wine cellar of ordinary domestic wine, which those who knew said was "not so bad." Every evening one or two bottles were consumed.

André, Joe, and I always enjoyed quiet evenings listening to a collection of records that Joe had taped in San Diego. He and Larry had set up a stereo tape recorder in the van so we could listen. André especially liked the music of Vivaldi, Purcell, Handel, and Bach. He was a practicing musician as well as an accomplished artist. Those who remember the Cousteau movie *The Silent World* will recall André playing his cello in the hot afternoon aboard the *Calypso*. He had more hair then but still the same quick smile. It was at sessions like this that I became attached to music of the Baroque era. We played

Handel's "Water Music" over and over. It was appropriate for such a barge as ours, even if we were a long way from the Thames.

The next day Dr. Guillermo P. Salas, "Bill," the director of the Geologic Institute at the University of Mexico, went down another of the tributaries into the canyon. He had been very helpful in making arrangements for our expedition to operate in Mexican waters. Dr. Salas thought that Mexican marine geologists might be interested in exploring their section of the continental shelf areas by submersible, so he decided to learn something of the techniques involved. His particular aim on this dive was to attempt to use a different reference system in tracking the *Saucer* and making observations that could be precisely located. It had bothered him that on the previous two dives we had been uncertain of the *Saucer's* location in relation to particular features in the canyon. He proposed a chart divided in a grid fashion. By following along a given contour on one wall of the canyon, the surface boat could tell him the quadrangle he was in and he could plot it on a similar chart in the *Saucer,* thus relating what he saw to his grid position.

On the dive it turned out that by using this method he could follow along a contour part of the time, but there were some discrepancies in the course heading. He noted a number of crevices running parallel to the canyon.

Dr. Shepard was ready for another dive on Wednesday, January 29, to investigate the steep slopes off the Tombolo near Dying Pelican Beach. We launched the *Saucer* in the beautifully clear water 30 meters deep over the sandy beach. It descended a sand chute and the divers observed only a trickle of sand flowing at depth. Slightly more than an hour had passed when we received instructions over the CB radio from *Shazam* to stand by for recovery. The *Saucer* was coming up slowly, without any power; the propulsion would not function. What was wrong with the propulsion motor? Gaston, like a fretful hen waiting for a stray chick, stood pensively on the stern smoking his cigarette, as always, down to nothing. He held the phone ready for the hookup diver to plug in so he could talk to André about the problem. Soon the *Saucer* surfaced, not very far from where it had started. The *Burch Tide* backed in toward it, came ahead to check her way, then we heard Earl boom the familiar "all stopped" over our P.A. system. This meant that the diver could get into the water, for the main propellers were secured.

Soon we had swung the *Saucer* aboard and were moving it around toward the cradle. Gaston conversed hurriedly with André. As he suspected, the motor had flooded, and the trouble was not the result of the switch failure that had occurred on Joe Curray's dive. A shadow of gloom was cast on our little group. Dr. Shepard felt shortchanged and rightly so—the dive had lasted an hour and five minutes and he had only begun its real mission. But once again the control rule had to be applied—a dive lasting more than one hour, even though aborted, is considered a completed dive. In this instance we had fulfilled the letter of the agreement, but we certainly hadn't kept our customer happy. Gaston, Ken, and Jerry carefully removed the 2-horsepower propulsion motor. It was becoming a routine operation to haul out the motor—an operation that both Ken and Jerry knew well. Soon after they had the motor apart, we could smell the odor of burned insulation. Apparently water had leaked in, as it had on dive 249, and had shorted the armature. Gaston and André spent many hours working over the motor case to make sure it was watertight. They put in a new armature and by late evening had the motor and case reassembled for installation in the morning. Fred had made sure to stock several of these motor armatures and fields. Two had come with the MATS shipment and he had one more sent from Marseille before we left for Mexico. Now one had been used, the second was in the motor, and one remained.

Shortly before noon Gaston announced to Fred that the motor was ready and André advised that the *Saucer* should make a short test dive to check the water integrity of the motor case. Fred tapped me to go along and "ride shotgun." This was the orientation dive for which I'd been waiting so long.

The dive was all too brief—about 20 minutes in 60 meters of water along a rather featureless sand bottom. It was long enough for André to check the performance of the motor and be satisfied that it worked. I enjoyed all 20 minutes. Now I could look anyone in the eye when queried as to whether I had made a dive in *La Soucoupe Plongeante.*

Back on the surface and aboard the *Burch Tide* we had a quick crew change, reloaded weights, double checked everything, and in a few minutes Canoe with "Bob-Dill," as Dill was called by the French, began dive 292 at the head of the canyon near the cannery. Bill Salas had reported what looked like some beach rock at 140 meters—far deeper than Bob had believed it to occur. It could, of course, be a displaced section moved down the canyon. Today Bob wanted to inspect this site more carefully. If there was beach rock still in place it would indicate a former sea level at that depth sometime in the geological past.

The *Saucer* moved down canyon without anything to report for about 30 minutes. A group of us sat on the stern of the *Burch Tide* basking in the sun. The next announcement over the P.A. system was like a bucket of cold water:

"The *Saucer* is on its way up. Stand by to recover it."

This time the dive, from start to finish, lasted one hour, give or take a minute depending on whose watch or clock was involved. Everyone was unhappy. Bob Dill had not really accomplished anything, and yet the dive was right on the one-hour margin. Further, it seemed as though there must be something basically wrong with the motor. Had they found the problem yesterday or had they perhaps overlooked something? Through the long afternoon of teardown, assessment, and diagnosis we all speculated gloomily about the future operations. It was difficult to see how we could run a diving service when we had such trouble keeping the vehicle operating.

We finally concluded that the motor case had not leaked but that the new armature had a faulty connection which caused excessive heating. This in turn burned out the motor components. Thus the trouble wasn't connected with the leakage of the day before. However, worse news was the fact that the final spare unit was also incorrect, and consequently unusable. Here we were, 750 miles from our nearest source of supply and repair. Part of our portability concept had been that we would carry the repair capability with us. However, winding motor armatures was far more than we had planned for on a ship this size. There seemed to be no solution but to send the motor to the States for repair. Fred made several radio-phone calls to various parts of the Westinghouse complex and waited for answers.

The rest of the customer group saw another long delay and unhappily packed their gear in preparation for a return to San Diego to wait for the *Saucer*'s repair. Bob Dill stayed on to do some exploratory scuba diving in an area of geological interest.

Later that afternoon it was decided that Jerry and Gaston should take all the armatures and fields to Los Angeles for rewinding. Fred had spoken to our Westinghouse Maintenance and Repair Shop in Compton, California, and they had agreed to rush the job over the weekend. Luckily, on the following day Jerry and Gaston were able to find space on the hotel plane to San Diego. They arrived at the Compton plant late that evening. It seemed doubtful that they would return by Monday as scheduled.

Meanwhile Tom Horton had flown in to visit with us for a few days and help us through our trying times—a job he performed well. We accused him, however, of waiting to come until we got to Cabo San Lucas, where the scuba diving was by far the best.

Again we were very much on "vacation," it seemed, with little work to do. Tom and I joined Bob Dill and John Theisen, Joe Thompson, and Ron Church to make a dive on the slope leading down to one of the canyon tributaries. We all donned our scuba gear. Wet suits were in order. Although the upper layers of water were delightfully warm, below 100 feet the temperature dropped considerably. Thompson, Theisen, and Church went as photographers, each with a different camera. Bob wanted them to photograph the condition of some stakes he had implanted the year before on the slope. On the first part of the dive, Dill and the photographers "bounce-dived" to 175 feet to inspect the rock wall quickly, to see if it was granite or beach rock. They returned shortly to report that it was granite, as suspected, but that they had seen a new canyon they hadn't known existed. Joe and John brought back some "black coral"—a valuable treasure that many divers hope to find. Ron Church had come to San Lucas to photograph the *Saucer* dives on a free-lance basis, although he had worked both with Westinghouse and NEL before on assignment. He brought with him an arsenal of cameras; they made Joe Thompson most envious.

The second part of the dive put us all down in about 60 feet of water on a fine silty slope. The object, Bob had explained, was to implant some new stakes into the bottom in a straight line. While one of us swam ahead putting in stakes, two others attempted to guide the placement and alignment. We had to be careful to move slowly and avoid stirring up the bottom. The visibility was only 20 to 30 feet. After we completed this task, Bob guided us down the slope and over a large rock outcropping. This turned out to be the beach rock he'd been describing from the *Soucoupe* dives. The bedding planes of it were easy to see as we swam first in front of it and then up along a fissure in the enormous block. It represented the only sedimentary rock in the area. We reached a maximum depth of 140 feet at the base of the outcrop.

Tom and one of the photographers had already departed for the surface. Tom had a strange habit of using about twice as much air as most divers. We used to kid him about it. In fact, once he used a set of double tanks, twice the regular volume of air, and returned with the same pressure reading as his buddy on a single tank. Some people use more air and others, like Joe and André, use much less. Soon I heard the characteristic ringing that my regulator makes as the air is getting low. I reached down to find my See-view gauge, as Bob and I began gradually working our way to the surface into the brightness of the upper world. I had been on reserve for a while and ended up with about 150 pounds of air. We returned to the *Burch Tide* to strip out of our gear and compare notes. Bob commented on the old stakes we had seen, which showed a definite trend downslope in places where the sediment was unstable and slowly creeping. He had used similar objects planted on the slopes, including old car bodies, in Scripps Canyon to show that the sediment on the steep slopes is moving measurably down into the canyons. Sometimes, of course, great hunks move out in slumps.

Like pigeons in the park coming for handouts, the pelicans congregated at the stern of the *Burch Tide* loudly asking for fish, bread, or anything edible. André spotted one pelican hungrily grabbing for the fish remains he was tossing them but unable to swallow anything. Looking closely, he saw that the bird's huge pliable pouch beneath his bill had been completely ripped where it joined the beak—perhaps in a fight or struggle for a fish with another pelican. The pelican submitted to being picked up and held on deck. Canoe went to his cabin for a needle and thread, then proceeded gingerly to sew the pouch together while the bird was held patiently. The operation took about 20 minutes and appeared to be successful. André cut him some morsels of fish and we opened his mouth and filled it. The pelican waddled to the stern, head tilted back, swallowing happily—a new bird. He plunked into the water. "Dr." Canoe was congratulated for his skill in saving a pelican from starvation. We thought we recognized the same pelican the next morning back at the feeding post.

We had heard that the pelicans suffered an occupational hazard. They plummet straight into the water, wings folded, and after many such dives their eyesight is damaged, and they finally go blind. In such a state they have difficulty obtaining food and sometimes starve. Perhaps some of the pelicans we saw on Dying Pelican Beach had been so afflicted.

Later that afternoon, while some of us were off on a diving excursion out at the end of the point, others took a walk to look at the night's haul in the shark-fishing industry. We had heard that sharks were prevalent in the local waters but so far had seen none either by scuba or *Saucer*. As we walked along the beach we came on a large collection of shark bodies the fishermen had hauled in that morning. There were 23 altogether and most of them were 6 or 7 feet long. Ron identified them as Galapagos sharks. Here on the beach the meat is cut off and sold, the jaws cut out as souvenirs, and the carcasses left for the pleasure of the buzzards.

With all the time on our hands we had a chance to meet some of the villagers. One good friend whom Bob Dill and John Houchen had known several years earlier was Keith Ross. I remembered hearing the name when we first came to San Lucas and thinking, "That's a strange name for a Mexican." When I met him I realized he was an Englishman. Keith had been in San Lucas for five years, having come from Canada and before that England. He was a mechanic and odd-jobs man who could do a bit of everything. For yachts coming into San Lucas needing repair, Keith was the man. He also acted as ship's chandler and provided all necessary supplies —even for the *Burch Tide*. He spoke fluent "Mexican," had a Mexican wife, and lived in a small and neat house in town. I gathered that he had been a mechanic in Canada but was attracted to the free and easy life in the village where he could go about in shorts, an old shirt, and bare feet. When we had first looked for him he had been off on one of his many trips to "the States," ferrying a sailboat north for her owner. This last trip had netted him a beautiful, shiny, but old Chevrolet pick-up truck in payment. Keith told us how he had driven it back from Santa Barbara in just over three days. Later, riding with him, I understood why he had been able to make such good time. He drove wildly down the sandy and bumpy roads at speeds I doubted possible.

Cruising sailboats and powerboats had started to come into San Lucas harbor on their way to winter cruises in the Gulf of California. This area was growing more popular each year. Some of the cruising people wanted to come aboard and see the *Saucer*, others would crowd around in small boats and watch during the operation. One yacht, however, was a permanent fixture in San Lucas Harbor—the *Goodwill*—famous for her trans-Pacific racing. She spent the entire winter moored in the harbor. A beautiful sight, she was a 161-foot schooner built in the days of the great yachts when the cost of crew and of upkeep was lower and a few people had more money. Her people often invited us over for cocktails and socializing. The main salon, which filled one side of the midships area, was spacious, with couches, tables, a piano, and bookcases. It was always thrilling to me to walk along the deck and try and imagine her under full sail with a stiff breeze making 12 or 13 knots!

One evening Larry and I left the *Goodwill* just before dusk to return to the *Burch Tide* for supper. As we came down onto the boat-landing platform we saw a great commotion not far from the ship. A herd of small whales or black fish was frantically swimming into the harbor. We started *Shazam's* motor to follow them and get a closer look. The water all around was churned up and every once in a while one or two whales would leap clear of the water. They turned short of the *Burch Tide* and began to swim at full speed out of the harbor. It was an impressive sight as some 150 to 200 animals swimming in close formation disappeared to sea. We guessed that they had been feeding on some smaller fish that they had chased into shallow water. We returned to the ship.

The next morning André was up early inspecting the motor housing of the *Saucer* to make sure that it would not leak again when the parts returned. He had poured some of the uncured silicone rubber around the inspection plate and its "O" ring, for this was a likely trouble spot. After he and Ken had put the housing and its shaft seal back on the *Saucer*, they decided it would be wise to make a trial dive, both to test the housing for water tightness and for us to experiment with hovering techniques in midwater.

It was Ken's turn to make the orientation dive with André, so that afternoon we took the *Saucer* 6 or 8 miles offshore in about 500 meters of water close to the area for the next series of dives. We were clear of any obstructions on the bottom and decided it would be safe to use a light tether on the *Saucer*. We took a large roll of polypropylene line in *Shazam* and just before launching shackled it to the *Saucer*. Canoe, Tom, and I went in *Shazam*. As the *Saucer* was released from the *Burch Tide* we paid out line. There was a slight current below and a contrary light wind on the surface, making it necessary for us to maneuver to keep over the *Saucer*. Even so, when we heard André say he was at 300 meters, we had paid out 500 meters of line. André and Ken remained at 300 meters for some time. We didn't have any strain on the line. It proved to us that the *Saucer* could stay at selected depths with very small changes in water ballast. After about an hour the *Saucer* started a slow ascent as we brought the line in hand over hand. Ken had the record of the deepest and longest of the crew's test dives. Further, and of greater importance to our diving, the motor housing proved to be dry and watertight.

On Monday the next group from NEL arrived by water. Eric Barham, Bob Bradley, and some other men had come down the coast in the Scripps T-boat, a converted Army 65-foot work boat called T-441. On the way they had made numerous observations and scuba dives at various locations along the rugged Baja coast.

Eric Barham was planning to make a series of dives to study the Deep Scattering Layer (DSL) he had begun investigating in December with the *Saucer*. After his success in using the *Saucer* to study the individual organisms, he was looking forward to observations where the DSL was known to be more concentrated. Eric had made several dives in *Trieste I* to try to study the scattering animals, but that large vehicle descended through the water too fast for good observations.

To our surprise and pleasure, Jerry and Gaston flew in Tuesday afternoon with the motor armatures newly rewound. They had chartered a light plane from San Diego. The turn-around time at the repair plant was quick and we could get the *Saucer* back on the line sooner than most of us suspected possible. After a check-out dive in the harbor late Tuesday, we were ready again. I had a feeling that everything was going to be fine now, because we'd already been through so much trouble that little else could go wrong. We became a little stale on our paid holiday and were eager to return to work and try to make up the lost time. At best it seemed that we would have to make up several dives—those short trips for Drs. Dill and Shepard.

On Wednesday the first dive was scheduled to be in the water no later than 0500, in order to be in the midst of the DSL organisms that came to the surface at night and left at first light. At 0320 the anchor chain began its monotonous and metallic clanking as it came aboard and I awoke with a start. This was to be my first day's trial at running the operation in preparation for taking over when Fred left at the end of the month. The whole procedure always went very smoothly and everyone knew his job; however, as happens when anything is attempted for the first time, I was a little uncertain. I went forward, grabbed a cup of hot coffee, and walked up on the foredeck. The ship got underway, quietly gliding down the harbor in the darkness under a clear black sky. I could just see my old friend, the fabled Southern Cross, above the horizon. Looking down at the bow wave, I could see a distinct glow of phosphorescence.

Within 40 minutes we were on station. There was a definite swell running and a breeze of 10 knots. When *Shazam* was put over the side we could see the size of the swell as we passed the tracking equipment to Larry. The *Burch Tide* lay quietly as the small boat bobbed and banged against the side. After some last-minute checks on the *Saucer* everything appeared in readiness. Eric Barham looked very dashing as he hurried into the *Saucer* wearing a heavy sweater and sporting a gray Hemingway-style beard. A quarter mile away we could see the running lights of T-441 rolling moderately as she lay to in the trough. Her mission was to measure accurately the DSL and report the depth of the main layer—from the Precision Depth Recorder (PDR) to us. In turn *Shazam* would tell Eric where the main and secondary layers of animals were. It was 0455. I took the hand CB radio that we used to con the bridge and pressed down the key:

"OK, Earl, we're ready to launch. You can bring the stern around a little into the wind, please."

The twin screws shot a wash of water to the side as the stern turned smoothly around.

"All stopped," came the reply over the P.A.

I walked around to see if Gaston was ready. He gave me the thumbs-up OK. I signaled to Ken in the crane and with a nod he brought the boom into action. Up and around went the *Saucer*. With the lights from the crane I could see the water now, so it was easier to judge the frequency of the waves. The trick, Fred had explained, was to launch the *Saucer* at the crest of a wave. I paused and counted several—Ken could see better and was doing the same. At the right moment I gave him a down sign and the crane lowered the *Saucer* as I gave a tug on the release line—the hook gave its click sound and the *Saucer* was free on the tag line. Not so bad, I thought to myself—but the hookup wouldn't be so simple. Dive 295 was off and running. The *Saucer* turned its lights on just after leaving the surface, creating a beautiful sight as the floodlights cast a large pale-blue halo around the hull in the surrounding black background.

Eric Barham hoped to make four such dives in two days—two morning and two evening—to observe the migrations of animals at successive dives. He planned to use practically no propulsion and to conserve lights, so that we might get two four-hour dives separated by eight hours on deck, which allowed for some battery recharge.

The *Saucer* descended slowly to 75 meters, with Dr. Barham observing as they went. The first scattering organisms were siphonophores, a type of jellyfish. At this point they were surrounded by many lantern fish and some squid. On the surface the PDR on T-441 began to show the various layers. This information was passed to the people in the *Saucer* by underwater telephone, so they could be sure to position themselves as the layers began to migrate down with the coming of daylight. The *Saucer* moved to about 140 meters, where it hovered for several hours making observations. To conserve battery power and keep from attracting unwanted organisms, the lights were switched on for two minutes and off for three.

The first observable downward movement came in the jellyfish and the lantern fish, but this was in Dr. Barham's opinion a very subtle migration, with only several organisms in view at one time. Another animal, which was somewhat of a surprise, was the small pelagic crab, which was seen at several levels. After some time, when it was clear that the main body of the DSL had migrated past her at 140 meters, the *Saucer* moved on down to 270 meters. On the way the occupants observed a few shrimp, prawn, and other euphausids, but never in any great concentration. The surface ship reported that the upper layers had moved to 270 meters and extended to 350 meters. About this time Dr. Barham began to see some lantern fish and then, at 300 meters, there were literally hundreds of these fish. After a while the *Saucer* started slowly up by pumping out water ballast for a controlled ascent. Apparently the *Saucer* "dragged" the lantern fish with it if the lights were left on. Once the lights were off, however, the fish no longer stayed with the *Soucoupe*, but departed. As it rose to 75 meters, some large scattering organisms were noted by the PDR on the surface boat, but strangely, at this depth those in the *Saucer* saw nothing at all.

Just above this layer were some large heteropods, mollusks, which Dr. Barham had never seen in the water before. Along with these were two of the pelagic crabs. The *Soucoupe* rose very slowly up through the water column, finally arriving on the surface after five hours and five minutes.

Fred let me continue to handle the dive when it came to recovery, which was of course made simpler by daylight. To my surprise the hookup went without a hitch.

Once all were on board we headed for the harbor, put the batteries on charge, reserviced the *Saucer,* and took a short snooze until 1530. Then the ship got underway again for the diving site so that the *Saucer* would be in the water just before sunset to make sure Dr. Barham would see the same organisms as they began to migrate back toward the surface. As is true of many other migrations of animals, we needed to know a great deal more in order to discover the reasons for these bold journeys.

The next three dives ran well, but, as in any continuous sort of observation, one event telescopes into the next. We slept for three or four hours and were again on duty for another long dive. Dr. Barham was a very intense observer and had great endurance, but at the end of the fourth dive even he was a little punchy. Since the dives were quite similar in every way I had not debriefed him on all of them. He summarized by saying that he felt the four successive dives were most valuable. He was sure that the layer that rose to the surface on one evening would certainly be the same organisms descending the next morning, and this knowledge helped identification. There was one exception: the pelagic crab seen on the first dive was absent on the fourth.

Dr. Barham commented about the crabs, "It's rather interesting, because they're not swimming actively. They just sit there with their appendages spread out in front of them. If you bother them with a light—they'll move a little and stop. Yet somehow they've been able to regulate their buoyancy so that they drift slowly down or up depending on the direction of migration. Perhaps they change their oil content or possess some sort of mechanism that no one has suspected. The main layer is myctophids or lantern fish. We caught them several times in plain view, so there's no doubt in my mind."

Dr. Barham felt that these observations may have been the first successful attempts to correlate the echo sounder traces of the DSL with the actual *in-situ* observations and pictures of individual organisms. He was pleased with the way in which he could use the *Saucer* as a platform and how closely the fish could be observed. The migration was so subtle that if not keenly observed it could be missed. I totaled our dives and hours and told Tom Horton that we had logged 14 operating hours in an elapsed time of 38 hours. We had never had so much use of the *Saucer* in so short a time.

After that almost continuous activity we rested briefly and regrouped for Doug Inman of Scripps, who planned to make several dives in San Lucas and farther up the coast in a canyon in Los Frailes harbor. Dr. Inman made a dive down the canyon on a track similar to that of Dill and Shepard. He found evidence of fairly strong currents in the main canyon in ripple marks, scour indications, and the presence of cobbles.

Unlike other investigators in previous dives he recorded currents up to .4 knot at 300 meters. Other than this his results were not particularly outstanding, but the dive held special meaning for the Westinghouse-OFRS crew. This was dive 300 for *Soucoupe Plongeante* 300. The French always celebrated every 50th dive in some special way. This time, when pilot Kientzy and Dr. Inman returned, they were greeted with a loud cheer, the usual cups of hot cocoa, and a blinding glare of flashbulbs from Joe's and Ron's cameras. The dive had finished late in the afternoon, so Little Joe had prepared a steak barbecue for all. To top it off, our good chef had spent many hours making a cake in the shape of the *Saucer,* topped with yellow frosting, noodles for jets, and pieces of candy for hardware. It was a real masterpiece, which was admired, photographed, and finally eaten.

That evening there was to be a town fiesta and celebration. Just before dark the *Deepstar* crew strolled over to the village to a hall where the activity was beginning. While we stood debating whether or not to enter, one of the young hostesses invited us to come in. There was a small admission charge. The brightly lit room was perhaps 40 by 60 feet and lined with benches. On one side of the room beer and soft drinks were sold. We could hear the generator chugging away out back. The people were mostly teenagers with a goodly number of dueñas sitting grimly on the sidelines. Our team collected in the corner and watched. The music was provided by records that were a mixture of Mexican rock-and-roll and folksong. Gradually the hall filled with many townspeople whom I recognized. Ron had found out that the fiesta was a yearly affair celebrating the good fortune of the port of San Lucas and the progress of the town.

Later, the port director related the achievements of the port and compared it with a neighboring fishing village down the coast. The ceremony was topped off by the crowning of a port Queen—a very lovely young girl who, by some strange chance, was the daughter of the port director. She was, however, the outstanding beauty of San Lucas. She made the rounds selling flowers (and dances). Gaston, with true European gallantry, bought a flower and instead of keeping it asked her to wear it.

The dives during the following week were made for Scripps biologist Dr. Rosenblatt, Professor Presbituro of the University of Mexico, John Houchen, and finally Bob Dill. The last two dives were among the most interesting—partly because we moved to a new site and also because the dives went very well. Bob had been looking forward to diving at Los Frailes; on earlier expeditions he and other diving geologists had made numerous scuba dives in the heads of the canyons there. Now he wanted to go deeper to observe any evidence of submarine erosion, sediment movement into deeper water, or overhanging walls.

Los Frailes, or The Friars, is a secluded spot on the coast about 45 miles northeast of Cabo San Lucas. The extremely steep hills extend to the water on the northeast, while a long crescent-shaped beach forms a harbor. The beach front slopes into the water so abruptly that it was possible to put the bow of the ship on the sand while having ample water aft. A fairly low beach ridge was backed up by some low hills and, farther inland, a group of low angular mountains. There was no sign of habitation. One abandoned building in poor repair stood just back of the beach. Bob told us that there was a small settlement about half a mile beyond. If we had time after the dive we should pay it a visit, he said. Now we were all for getting dive 308 on its way.

Bob explained that he knew that the sediments he had observed earlier at the heads of the tributaries are transported into deep water, because this same sediment had been sampled in 9,000 feet of water. The last known flushing of the canyon had taken place in 1962 in a large storm. Although there had been three storms since, there was no evidence that large amounts of sediment had moved out of the canyon.

The *Saucer* started in a very narrow tributary some 5 meters wide that soon formed a small hanging tributary to a larger one. This tributary was on the western side of the Bay of Los Frailes. The *Saucer* then moved down the steep walls covered with gorgonian corals, where Bob reported very poor visibility of 10 to 15 feet. The passage became very narrow. Several times the *Saucer* had to reverse, back out, and go over the overhangs. The depth was 55 to 60 meters. The canyon was asymmetrical, with the steepest slope on the outside of the meandering channel. The overhangs were more pronounced toward the bottom of the channel. The visibility continued poor as the divers descended, due mostly to organic matter, plankton, and a gelatinous-looking substance.

In *Shazam* John Houchen and I tried to map the *Saucer's* course. I was kept busy shooting sextant angles every four or five minutes as well as steering the boat. John ran the tracking transducer and operated the telephone and CB radio. The *Saucer* reported frequently and was constantly moving.

The plankton appeared to be diatom chains, one-celled plants, that were bioluminescent when the light was switched off. The *Saucer* came through a very distinct thermocline or thermal boundary at about 80 meters, where the visibility improved sharply. The temperature dropped from 16° C. to 13° C. At 170 meters the main canyon opened out, becoming quite broad—perhaps 25 meters across. This was a junction of three tributaries. The slope of the bottom for almost the entire dive was 20°, except in the area of slump scars and several reversals in depressions. In one of these areas, around a sort of dune, a large rounded cobble, which lay among coarse sands, gravel, and fine grain shells, was picked up with the mechanical arm of the *Saucer*. It looked more like a slump deposit that had been carried down rather than a product of current movement. These cobbles were found at 255 meters.

Bob reported that some areas of the walls had a deep brown growth that extended toward the base. Here there were clean, freshly worn spaces. These fresh spaces on the walls were above the slump scars; consequently, it looked as though the fresh rock walls may have been exposed by slumping. No currents in excess of 0.1 knot were observed. The gorgonians extended all the way to 265 meters, the deepest part of the dive, although they were less abundant farther down. The rocks did not have the organically roughened surface that is common in shallower water, where organisms are cutting away the granite. At greater depth, however, the over-hangs indicated that something was cutting away the base of the rocks. No evidence was apparent of the block avalanche like those observed in San Lucas. The bottom below 200 meters appeared very inactive, with about an inch of fine sediment covering everything. Just before the *Saucer* came up, Bob reported a beautiful slump scar. The material had broken away very recently—after the deposition of the fine-grain sediment layer. This probably indicated that there had been some movement, not, however, caused by currents. At 205 meters Bob reported seeing a shark—it was 5 to 6 feet long, swimming along slowly.

We had lost track of time. More than four hours had gone by and now the *Saucer* was due to come up. It had been an interesting dive for us on the surface, for there had been much to listen to in the way of observations. Later, summing up after the dive, Bob concluded that the significant finds of that dive had been the definite overhangs in the granite walls along the canyon floor, the recently exposed granite walls, the rounded beach cobbles at 255 meters, and the slumps. Taken together, these phenomena certainly indicated transport of sediment by means other than currents. This transport was definitely modifying the canyon. Such observations shed new light on the nature of the mechanisms that transport sediment in the sea.

The "going-ashore" party was formed. Bob said that the villagers in the settlement had very little food and had to travel a long way for supplies. Little Joe had been waiting for an opportunity to get rid of certain supplies left over from the time the *Burch Tide* was in her home port of New Orleans. These included rice, beans, hot sauce, peppers, and other Cajun fare that he couldn't "sell" to our group. So, we carried several cartons of food ashore with us and followed a path among the hills. There were several pastures with a few cattle. To contain the cattle the natives used a crude but effective thorn fence made of the local cactus. This would discourage the most determined beast, and also made walking at night hazardous if one got caught in a cactus patch.

The village consisted of several dwellings with thatched roofs and sides. One large hut was the common kitchen for the community. Here the women and children were at work. The hearth in front of the fire was clean and worn by use. Some of the women were grinding meal in a large mortar. Until several years before our arrival there were only men at Los Frailes, but now as the settlement prospered women and children were sent there to help settle the wilderness. It was a long journey by land over the hills to the north. These people were pleased to receive our gifts and showed us around their farm, which abounded with pigs, chickens, and goats.

We moved on, making a large circle around toward the beach as the sun got closer to the horizon. Out across a field that had been farmed were the remains of a house. It had belonged to a rancher who had died, but was now abandoned. Most of it had been blown over by the fierce *chubasco*, the screaming north wind of the winter that blows for days in gusts up to 110 miles an hour. Nearby was a well of good water in a grove of palm trees. What a waste it seemed for good water to be unused in such a dry wasteland. The doorstep to the house was an enormous grinding stone on which the meal and flour had been ground. Lying next to it was the smoothly shaped stone pestle that fitted against the hollow of the mortar. I could not resist this artifact, so I added it to my collection of other stones, bits of driftwood, and flotsam.

My treasure trove was nothing compared to that of André. He was continually collecting coral, gorgonians especially, and shells that he hung to dry in the sun or secreted away under one of the vans like a dog with a prize bone. After a week or so the smell from drying corals was overpowering. At every possible chance he had gathered dried pelican bones from Dying Pelican Beach and strung them together. When he departed for France we were left with this legacy of bones, shells, wood, and coral, and, oh yes, how could I forget the cow's head with some of the cow still attached. Since André couldn't cart this collection home he had hoped to ship it with the *Saucer*. André's departure had been sudden—much like his arrivals. I assumed that Captain Cousteau had asked him to return to assist in the next prolonged submergence experiment, *Conshelf III*. André was to be the leader of that adventure in undersea living.

Our last dive in Mexico was for Bob Dill again, who continued his observations of Los Frailes Canyon. Upon completion we broke camp and headed back to San Lucas to take our departure. Over a six-week period, despite our several breakdowns, the OFRS-Westinghouse team had made 31 dives of from 20 minutes to 5 hours duration. Twenty-three of these were for scientists. The geologists explored and delineated the canyons and the biologists studied the DSL and local fauna. For these scientists there remained hours of intensive study of the photographs, movies, sediment samples, and dive tape-recording logs. These data would provide the basis for scientific and technical papers to be written for journals and presented at meetings. For us, the Mexican series had been excellent experience in the sort of field problems that any operational group must expect, and be prepared to solve. We learned that our arrangement to count the number of dives per month as the standard of our performance in fulfilling our contract was severely penalizing to us and should be changed on future diving jobs. We still believed that a portable, movable, diving service such as ours was an important contribution to underwater exploration. We were now ready for the next step in the program, which would start in several weeks and would involve making special underwater sound measurements.

We flew out over Cabo San Lucas for the last time on our way to La Paz, then San Diego. Fred felt that the operation was running properly and that he could leave it in my hands. As soon as we returned to San Diego, he and Val were going to Baltimore for other assignments. This left our team short-handed but meant that I could probably expect at least one or two replacements. For me there was much to look forward to in taking over the operation.

Noises in the Sea

While we had been away in Mexico, Ken and Val had worked on the design of a special rig for the U.S. Navy Underwater Sound Laboratory (USN/USL) and had built a framework to support a large noise-measuring array that the *Saucer* would carry. Six months earlier Val and I had discussed with the USL engineers the general configuration of the mount and how they wanted to make their measurements. Several sketches of the frame had resulted but since there were some unknown dimensions about the structure of the *Saucer* a formal drawing had not been made. Part of the design required that the framework could be jettisoned if the *Saucer* got fouled in anything. Val had decided therefore that explosive bolts would be the best fastenings.

The *Burch Tide* arrived the following Monday and we accomplished four scheduled dives by the end of the week.

After the last dive, which was for Dr. Shepard, we began the conversion of the *Saucer* for the USN/USL dives. Ken made the last-minute measurements and fitted the frame on the *Saucer*. This meant that the two forward upper fiberglas fairings had to come off for the frame to bolt in. The frame was the foundation for a 10-foot boom supporting a perpendicular noise-measuring array that measured 15 feet. In addition, the Sound Laboratory wanted the array to rotate through 90 degrees—from horizontal to vertical—so that any measuring instruments, such as the hydrophones that were on the array, could detect sound in both planes. For rotation we used a light hydraulic actuator strong enough to move the boom. The *Saucer* had one spare hydraulic line, which Ken connected to it. Ken, who was a good machinist, cut and fit the four-legged frame on the bow of the *Saucer*. I had told him that he could take a week's leave if the frame was ready for USL. He had been away from his family since Christmas, and left for Norfolk that evening.

The USN/USL crew arrived on Saturday to begin fitting their equipment onto and inside the *Saucer*. This group hailed from New London and included nine men who were to dive, collect, reduce data, and assist in the month's diving schedule. There were several counterparts at NEL, who were also involved in sound measurements and who hoped to make dives with us later, using the same equipment. Thus the USL people were able to call in NEL for help in machine-shop facilities and electronics work if they needed it.

Late Saturday night my family arrived in San Diego after a trying flight from Boston and a long bus ride from Los Angeles because the fog prevented a local landing. It was 3 AM when we got home to La Jolla and I was blissfully asleep when I was awakened the next morning by a telephone call from Ralph Austin, the leader of the USN/USL group.

"Sorry to bother you, but it looks as though we have problems with that frame you guys put on. Ed and I don't think it can possibly work the way it is. Maybe you'd better come over and see what we mean," Ralph explained.

"Sure," I said in a daze. "Be over in about an hour."

I drove my scooter to the NEL pier, where a crowd of engineers and technicians was standing around the *Saucer*. Gaston and Canoe were there too, aghast at the amount of gear that had to go aboard the Saucer.

"You see," Ed April said, pointing to the framework, "the boom will never rotate the way this actuator is set up. Further, I doubt that these bolts can all be trusted to explode. What if one hung up? The rig probably would stay on. And it really looks sort of flimsy for the weight of the boom and array." He pointed to the long 2-inch aluminum tubing and the longer T-shaped crosspiece that held the hydrophone array.

"You may be right," I said looking at the mounting. "We didn't have a chance to try it out, because we finished our last scientific dive just yesterday. What do you suggest?"

"Well, maybe we can beef up the structure and remount the actuator. I'll have to work on a way to release the array and possibly keep the framework on the *Saucer*. It'll take another day or two, though."

"OK," I said, somewhat dejected. We had hoped to get several dives in before the end of the month to make up for time lost on the journey from San Lucas. As it was, we had just made the minimum number of 15 dives for February. Transit time from San Lucas counted against us.

Turning to other things, I found that Gaston had removed all the equipment that would not be used, so as to save weight. These dives were going to be quite different from all past ones since there would be no need for lights, photography, the arm, or the tape recorder. Gaston had been busy taking out the spare oxygen bottle, the pinger receiver, flashing light control, movie camera, and batteries. This equipment alone weighed 50 pounds. Outside, he and Jerry had removed and weighed the arm, current meter, spotlight, 35mm camera, and spare ballast weights, for a total of 111 pounds before submersion.

Inside the *Saucer* in place of the usual equipment, the USL group had to include an amplifier, batteries, terminal board, oscilloscope, differential depth gauge, and a meter, for a total of 113 pounds, a weight almost equal to what we took out. On some of the experiments to be performed a 7-channel tape recorder was required. Outside the *Saucer* there was an additional 35 or 40 pounds in boom and hydrophones. As a result neither the USL observer nor the pilot could weigh more than 165 pounds. The installation and fitting of all this equipment took another day and a half. Mindful of the versatility of the *Diving Saucer,* we were able to make these drastic changes.

On Monday, with the assistance of Ed April and other USL people, the frame was reinforced and pronounced barely satisfactory, although Ed still had some ideas for improving it. By Tuesday everything seemed ready for a balancing test dive using this ungainly rig. There was just room to make a launch at the NEL pier where we were moored. The crane could swing the *Saucer* and the USL boom past the next ship and let it sit in the water. For proper balance in the experiment we needed a passenger. Little Joe had been bugging us for months to let him have a ride in the *Saucer.* Now it was his turn. He was delighted, even though he was to be in it only for a short while. After the vehicle was on the tag line and the fore and aft stability looked fine, Canoe called for the *Saucer* to be released. They sank to 20 feet and had a chance to feel how the *Saucer* behaved in the water and on the bottom with this long "nose" in front. We had a diver standing by in case something became fouled in the debris of the harbor. Twenty minutes later the *Saucer* was retrieved and Little Joe emerged with a big smile—he was now a full fledged saucernaut.

The next morning we left early for the operating area. After a lot of searching and consulting with the Navy, a general site had been carefully selected that would be fairly quiet and no deeper than 300 meters. It was a spot about 30 miles south of San Diego. This put us in Mexican waters again and required the consent of the Mexican government, even though we would be 6 to 8 miles offshore. Luckily, however, we didn't have to clear and enter port with the customs authorities of San Diego for each trip to the operating area.

By 1030 we were on station. The weather was fine and the sea calm. After about an hour's delay there seemed to be problems in assembling the rig. The breakaway arrangement consisted of a hinged retainer around the end of the boom. When the mechanical arm actuator was contracted, it pulled a line that released a ring on the hinge. As an additional safety factor, Gaston connected a cable from the emergency weight to the release mechanism so that if the hydraulic actuator failed there was a mechanical method available. It was all very clever, but now, as we assembled it and gave it a try, it balked. The aluminum surfaces didn't work smoothly. The rig still was not properly designed for the job. Canoe refused to dive until the problems were corrected. He and Gaston argued—but Canoe was right and since he was our only pilot we had to listen to his suggestions. Reluctantly I informed Ralph and Ed that the framework wasn't acceptable and that in the interest of safety we should return to port and attempt a better design.

The rest of the week was spent building a sturdier framework at the NEL shop. The breakaway mechanism was redesigned with the help of Canoe and Gaston. A new concern arose over the whole jettison procedure as we examined the way it should work. After several dry runs the separation of the seven signal leads from the array where they joined the wire harness going through the hull looked uncertain. It seemed doubtful that the connectors would pull free if the array became caught and the *Saucer* had to escape. We turned to the existing technology of space hardware. A firm in Los Angeles made an explosive cable cutter endorsed by the National Aeronautics Space Administration (NASA) and used reliably on space vehicles. It clamped around a bundle of cables and upon firing an explosive squib a cutting edge would guillotine the wires. Larry was our adviser on this device since he had worked with a variety of explosives in the Navy. Four cutters were rush ordered and upon receipt of them we tested one at the NEL pressure-test facility. After several cycles to 1,000 psi in the tank, Larry hooked it up and made a test firing in water. The charge went off sharply but with very little "kick" or reaction. These cutters were designed not to impart any undue force that would affect the stability of a space vehicle. I could see that Canoe was a bit skeptical about the gadget. Larry explained carefully how highly reliable the cutter was, because it had two parallel firing circuits in case one didn't work. Canoe still looked unconvinced. I suspected that the longer someone was around the water and working in it, the more skeptical he became of clever devices. It was true that many things never worked as advertised. However, we were fairly sure this safety device would work if it was needed. We hoped it wouldn't be.

By Sunday evening all of the framework, its release mechanism, and the cable cutter were installed. We had demonstrated that the array could be easily dropped by the activation of the arm actuator. As a further back-up, a line had been attached to the 400-pound emergency weight that would release the boom and array. If the hydraulic circuit failed, the release of the emergency weight, which was done mechanically, would drop the whole works.

Undaunted by our delays and ready to make some dives, we steamed out of San Diego at 0600 Monday morning, March 1. The plan was to make a dive at the site, Bahia Descanso, remain there overnight, get an early dive the next day, and then return to port. Ralph Austin and I decided this schedule would be best since it allowed USL to inspect and reduce their data ashore, where the proper equipment was. If there were poor data or some unsuspected problem with the equipment, the scientists would want to know the condition and correct it before another dive. I had hoped to stay on station three or four days running and avoid the six hours of travel by ship, but the two days and one evening plan seemed better, since we were still uncertain if any of the USL equipment would work.

The observer for the first dive was Gerry Assard from the acoustical group at USL. He explained to Canoe how he wanted to make the dive.

"As soon as we leave the surface," he said, "the *Burch Tide* will move away and leave the small boat standing by. As soon as it gets quiet I'll turn on my equipment and see if we pick up any sound. Probably it'll be so noisy that I can't even turn it on until we reach 100 meters. When we get to 300 meters I'll have the hydrophones working and ready to measure."

Canoe nodded. So far it seemed simple enough.

"Then," continued Gerry, "you'll have to stabilize the *Saucer* at 300 meters and secure all machinery while we record in the vertical position. The *Saucer* must stay within 15 feet over a 15-minute period."

Canoe had perfected the art of slowly drifting the *Saucer* a few inches a minute while piloting for Dr. Barham. Now it was crucial to maintain the vertical control for at least 15 minutes.

"After 15 minutes we rotate the array from vertical to horizontal, then measure again. Finally, in the last measuring period, I want the *Saucer* to turn 90 degrees in the horizontal. In this way, we can isolate and correlate a possible sound target. Then we move up to 150 meters and 100 meters and repeat the process."

Canoe smiled. "It is possible, but may be very difficult. Wait and see."

Gerry and I walked toward the *Saucer* as the ship began to slow down as it approached the spot Ralph had picked out on the chart near a sounding of 178 fathoms.

"Tell me something about the purpose of the dive and how the equipment will function," I said to Gerry.

"These six hydrophones are geometrically spaced to give the optimum arrangement possible in the 15 feet of array. They're attached to the aluminum tube and each one has a lead, as you can see here, coming back to the hull penetrator. These phones are extremely sensitive. The signals received are passed through filters and amplified and then recorded. Inside I can listen and watch the meters of each phone."

"And how does the rotation of the boom fit into the measurements?"

"Well, we're trying to measure ambient noise—the noise that's always in the ocean, uncontaminated by other ships, submarines, or even the *Saucer*'s own noise. We've picked a spot where we think we're protected by the horseshoe-shaped bay and a high ridge. If we take two measurements in the horizontal separated by 90 degrees and we don't get the same correlation when we plot it on a correlogram, then we'll know that there was a target, although perhaps we wouldn't know exactly where it was. If there is no target—even a ship at 15 or 20 miles can cause a detectable noise—then our measurements aren't any good. We think the *Saucer* will be a good quiet platform."

"I see. It does sound like a new approach. I thought you people had made a lot of ambient sea-noise measurements from the surface or from buoys. Aren't these valid?"

"Yes, we've made a lot of such measurements, but the noise of the cables from the surface, the ship, or other unavoidable noise has interfered. We've never made correlation measurements as successful as those we hope to make here. Neither has anyone else."

"The echo sounder says 77 fathoms," announced Earl over the P.A. "Is this a good spot for it?"

I picked up my CB handy talkie. "Looks OK from here. How far to the ridge?"

"About four miles."

"All right, we're here."

Ralph and I had discussed the necessity of getting the *Burch Tide* away from the area, since it made a great deal of noise, even when drifting. The skipper didn't want to secure his main engines and it was necessary for one generator to be always in operation. There wasn't any such thing as a "quiet ship" that is used by research vessels doing acoustic work. We had to move away. This meant, of course, that in case of an emergency the *Burch Tide* was going to be 15 to 20 minutes away. We picked out a spot where a long, narrow, and steep submarine ridge ran, forming the broad bowl of Descanso Bay. It certainly looked as though it isolated the bottom from most noise out in the ocean. The area looked completely desolate and void of ships, but the principal steamer route lay off 6 to 8 miles to seaward and might give the acoustic group trouble. For the other scientists later in the week who wanted to observe electro-magnetic noise, these precautions were less important.

Everything was ready and Gerry climbed into the *Saucer* amid the maze of gear now on the observer's side. He sat faced aft and monitored the instruments that were lashed onto the water tank. He had no need to look out the port and by sitting he put his weight in the middle of the *Saucer*. Canoe had cautioned him to sit very still during the quiet period so as not to disturb the balance of the *Saucer*.

We had moved the *Saucer* from its normal position facing forward around to facing the starboard quarter, to allow the array to be fitted. The array stuck out over the side and could clear the ship as the *Saucer* was swung over the stern. At this point Canoe rotated the boom to put the array into a vertical position that would cause much less strain on the rig when the *Saucer* was launched. The sea was the usual calm water, with the long, low swell that we were so accustomed to. I told Ken to lower away and released the hook. The *Saucer* slipped into the water gracefully, with its T-shaped boom protruding. Gaston indicated that everything was OK and the diver cut it loose. We waited for a minute or two, then moved off to the west at full speed, leaving *Shazam* with Jerry Burnett and a USL companion to guard the *Saucer*. Tracking was hardly necessary, as the *Saucer* moved very little. Of course, if the small boat drifted in the wind, they had to reposition. At first, this seemed a difficult task. Six miles offshore there were very few points of reference for *Shazam*.

After several miles I could just make out *Shazam* in the distance as I stood squinting into the sun on the bridge. We were now 8 or 10 miles offshore. Soon the echo-sounder trace began to drop off, showing that we had passed over the top of the ridge. Earl stopped the engines as we coasted for a while.

"I make it about 4.7 miles," he said. "It took us 24 minutes to get here. How's your radio contact with *Shazam*?"

"I'll try it."

"*Shazam—Burch Tide*," I spoke into the microphone of the

radio, looking to see if I could spot the white hull of *Shazam*. I couldn't.

"*Burch Tide*—this is *Shazam*. Read you loud and clear. How me?"

"Real good here, Jerry. I hear you, but I can't see you."

"OK. The *Saucer* reports that they had too much sea noise even to attempt to check their gear at 100 meters. They're going on to 300 meters and should be there now."

There! I caught sight of *Shazam* finally and marked the spot against a notch in the hills and mountain behind. Over the next two hours we got occasional reports from the *Saucer* via *Shazam*. A light breeze had sprung up and *Shazam* began to drift. Its occupants could not start the motor to maintain position during the measuring period because its sound interfered. If they weren't sure when one of the periods ended, it became even worse. It was during the in-between periods that *Shazam* had to move back over the *Saucer*. The telephone was important in keeping us informed of the measuring periods. Our telephone worked well only when the boat was directly over the *Saucer*, so drifting away complicated the situation quickly.

Now, however, *Shazam* reported receiving a message that the *Saucer* was on the way up because of troubles in the acoustic gear. We started after them. By the time we had arrived the *Saucer* had been on the surface ten minutes and *Shazam* was right alongside.

We sat and listened as Gerry Assard explained how the dive went. At the beginning of the dive the noise level from the small boat was so high that everything was off scale until about 150 meters. They continued on to 300 meters, but every time Gerry tried to make measurements there was a feedback in the hydrophones.

"What happened," said Gerry, "was that one hydrophone started to oscillate at about 500 cycles and then this coupled into the aluminum shaft and generated the same frequency to the next phone, and before I could handle the situation they all took off."

"Is there some way you can isolate this?" I inquired.

"I hope I can suspend the hydrophones on rubber to stop this, but there may be other electrical problems too."

"Did you ever find out if the system was working?" asked Ralph.

"I removed the phones and ran them directly into the filters and then into the amplifiers and I was able to hear something like background noise and when I knocked on the hull I could hear it on the amplifiers."

"How was the stability of the *Saucer*?" I asked. "Could you move around or did you have to sit very still?"

"I had a lot more freedom than I expected. I could reach over to the amplifiers without upsetting the balance. Canoe had turned off the motor, hydraulic pump, gyro, and water pump."

"The *Soucoupe* was very normal with this array and the ascent was no problem," Canoe added. "I think it will be OK."

They had been within 100 feet of the bottom and at first hadn't wanted to go any deeper until there was more confidence in maneuvering with the boom and little chance of snagging it. Now Canoe felt that the maneuvering would be less difficult. The *Saucer* was working out well as a platform, it appeared. If USL could only get the hydrophone rig to work we would all be pleased.

During the evening they worked to modify the hydrophones. By morning a strong northeasterly wind off the coast was steadily building up the sea to 4- or 5-foot waves. We stood on the bridge watching the wind gust to 30 knots and saw no chance of getting a dive in. Ralph thought we would do better to return home and try the next day, so we headed north. This was the first day we had lost to weather in 1965 and only the fourth or fifth throughout the entire program. With spring coming on we could expect blustery days.

Wednesday found us standing out of San Diego early into a bit of swell but not much sea. After all the wind of the previous day it was a delight to see a good diving day ahead. On the way to Descanso Bay we changed some of the *Saucer*'s interior equipment from acoustic to electromagnetic. The day's observer was Manuel Finkle, who headed the electromagnetic

(EM) group. Its equipment was similar to the acoustic group's instruments but involved in addition an oscilloscope and 7-channel tape recorder. The observer had to put the oscilloscope in his lap, because there was no other vacant spot. Manny was interested in recording electromagnetic noise in the sea, which he was going to measure in the spectrum from 5 to 1,000 cycles. Electromagnetic noise is generated in the atmosphere by lightning discharges, which, on a worldwide basis, build up to a noise level or background that can be detected for thousands of miles. One of the USL objectives was to measure the penetration and attenuation of these noises in seawater. At the same time, noises are also propagated through the earth and into the water. Most observations in this area of Extremely Low Frequency (ELF) have been made in the atmosphere, but few in the sea. USL has made measurements with towed devices in water, but none to depths of 1,000 feet. It is suspected that there are other factors which affect measurements by towed devices. Ocean currents may become conductors through the earth's field, interfering with measuring true EM signals. Also, telluric signals or those coming naturally from the earth, such as geomagnetic activities, may be added in some way.

The principal change to the outside rig was the substitution of a fiberglas array for the aluminum one. This array was also 15 feet long but had only 2 electrodes—one disc at each end as a sensor. Therefore there were only two leads. Part of the purpose of the EM dives was to compare the results by using electrodes of carbon, stainless steel, sintered bronze, and silver silver chloride.

"The dive should start with the *Saucer* hanging on a tether at 3 meters," explained Manny, "so I can calibrate my equipment. Then we can drop down to 300 meters and begin measuring. We won't need to rotate the boom, but we'll have to measure for 10 minutes at 30-meter levels all the way up."

We went through the launch procedure and after a short time at 3 meters released the *Saucer*. Larry took over the *Shazam* duty. Joe Thompson was in the water making still films and movies for the company documentary movie. I returned to the bridge to watch the operation and talk with *Shazam.* During the EM dives the *Burch Tide* moved only about a mile away, for its acoustic noise didn't affect these measurements.

I listened casually to the CB radio, which was at times very busy on the Channel 9 frequency. We had become very informal about our radio procedure in Mexico since there we rarely used call letters and often, what with the quick action and orders between the stern, the bridge, and *Shazam,* there wasn't time. If anyone from outside heard our conversations, he must have wondered what we were doing. On the other hand, we heard some pretty strange talk while we were monitoring calls from *Shazam.* On several occasions when the air was relatively quiet, a soothing voice, sounding like that of Walter Houston would come on quite loud and probably close by.

"This is the Old Trapper . . . just settin' here in my cabin in Nome, Alaska. The snow's pretty deep outside but it's right warm here."

The voice would go on in this way for some time, describing a fictitious scene, then stop for somebody to return the call. We never heard the other side of the conversation, which was probably beyond the range of our equipment. Later in the month we heard the same voice once as "the old fisherman," then as "a West Texas colonel." It helped to pass the time. We never did figure out what was going on.

Shazam's crew managed to stay fairly close to the *Saucer* by turning on their motor every 10 minutes to move up the distance they had drifted and maintaining telephone communication. There was little to report; the *Saucer* came up another 30 meters after every recording period. The saucernauts used the propulsion to move this distance, because it was faster than changing buoyancy. Finally, after three and a half hours, they came to 30 meters and held position for the *Burch Tide* to make a trial run over top to listen for ship interference. We moved over the spot slowly and the saucernauts reported that there was a decided disturbance, especially in the 60-cycle noise. This would be from our generators.

When the *Saucer* came aboard *Burch Tide,* Manny told me that all had gone well. He was pleased with the way in which they had been able to make the observations. There was no way for him to know whether the data collected were worthwhile until they were reduced from magnetic tape, on special equipment ashore at NEL, into a form easily evaluated and judged valid.

We lay to that evening offshore, with the intention of making another EM dive in the morning using a different electrode. It looked as though we were going to be able to maintain the schedule of two days out, return to port to change observers, then go out again. Possibly we could also double up and make two dives on the second of a series, but we found that such an undertaking became very strenuous for our only pilot. Fred had hoped that we could have Joe or Larry, now partly trained, try a dive or two when complicated bottom maneuvering wasn't involved. Canoe said the decision must be up to Captain Cousteau in France.

The EM group made three more dives and after a quick turnaround on Friday evening we decided to attempt our sixth dive of the week. The weather was good and we couldn't afford to slow down now. Gerry Assard had straightened out his hydrophones and after several checks was sure he had solved the oscillating feedback problem. Each phone was suspended by an elastic cord, isolating it from the metal boom and other hydrophones.

As we rounded the breakwater to head south from San Diego there was a moderate swell running, but at a fairly long period. By the time we arrived at Descanso Bay the sea had changed a little and it seemed as though we would be able to launch and recover, since there was no wind or waves on the long swells. I estimated that the height of the swell was probably 6 or 8 feet, but it was a very slow motion that the crane could adjust to and not difficult for a pickup.

We had decided that the best way to operate would be to place a marker buoy at the dive site and let *Shazam* use it as a reference or even tie on to it. This meant that if the *Saucer* descended near the buoy *Shazam* wouldn't have to use the motor in noisy periods. During quiet periods even the pinger had to be secured because of its interference. The EM group later reported that the pinger also put big spikes of noise on their records.

Gerry Assard climbed aboard and with little delay the *Saucer* was buttoned up and placed in the water. Everything was checked out, the *Saucer* cut loose, and Jerry Burnett was left in *Shazam* standing by. It was nearly noon and Little Joe started to serve lunch. The familiar "Chow is down, chow is down" came over the loudspeaker. Earl took *Burch Tide* about 2½ miles away to a spot closer to the ridge and one that seemed isolated from any noise. I stayed on the bridge to monitor the radio. Earl throttled back the engines to neutral and let the vessel drift to a stop while he made an entry in the ship's log at 1214. The radar reflector placed on *Shazam* stood out clearly on the radar screen. Earl left the bridge to get some lunch and Larry came up to relieve me just as we heard the familiar whistle on the radio. That couldn't be the *Saucer,* I thought. What goes on here? Then we heard Canoe's voice:

"*Burch Tide, Burch Tide—Soucoupe* on surface—emergency. Come quickly!"

I had a sinking feeling in my stomach. Here we were, miles away—in fact I had just checked the log—we were 16 minutes away. I first thought the trouble might be a fire. I spoke to Canoe.

"*Soucoupe—Burch Tide.* We are on our way. *Shazam,* are you there?"

"Roger, *Burch Tide.* We have attached the tow bridle."

Larry called down the companionway for Earl and Gaston while I shoved the throttle controls to Ahead Full and spun the wheel hard left. We were nearly around on course by the time Earl reached the bridge. He looked worried. We both felt that we should not have gotten so far away.

Gaston took the microphone and began to quiz Canoe on the condition of things. Shortly he said, "*Soucoupe* has water inside. Canoe says maybe 10 to 15 liters. They dropped emergency weight, but the release for the array didn't work. No real danger, but hurry."

Everybody was at his station as the *Burch Tide* backed up to the *Saucer* for retrieval. We saw what had happened. The array had released properly from the framework, but when Canoe dropped the 400-pound weight, it was still held by the cables from the hydrophones. It dangled beneath, limp and broken. The "highly reliable" cutter hadn't functioned. Before we could bring the *Saucer* aboard we had to secure the array. Larry was the diver and attached a line to it, then unplugged the connectors. We brought the *Saucer* aboard. I for one was never so glad to see it placed back in its cradle.

Gerry emerged smiling and looking as cool as ever. He was bathed in hydraulic oil and water and so was Canoe. Canoe's coveralls were soaked. He undressed by the washing machine, showered, then came back to the office to tell us about the dive.

On the way down the hydrophones appeared to be working fine. The *Saucer* reached 300 meters and leveled off. Canoe went through his routine of getting the water ballast trimmed just right so the *Saucer* would drift down 1 or 2 meters in the 15-minute quiet period. He then took a final reading on the gyrocompass and secured it. The hydraulic pump was turned off. Normally it would run when any hydraulic control or actuator is used. As designed, it always keeps the system at a pressure slightly over ambient sea pressure. All other machinery, including lights, was secured.

The two men settled down to making the first measurement and recording. It was very still inside the *Saucer* now that all the whirs and buzzes had been quieted. Suddenly there was an eruption of oil and water spurting over Canoe and Gerry. Water was rushing in from outside at a pressure of nearly 445 pounds per square inch. It wouldn't take long to fill the *Saucer* at that rate. Canoe guessed that the spare hydraulic line might have failed. In the darkness he reached with lightning action to shut off the control valve at the aft end. The leak stopped. He reached across Gerry, broke the safety strap, and turned the mechanical release for the emergency weight through its full turn. The *Saucer* jerked and began an extra fast ride toward the surface. By this time perhaps 20 seconds had elapsed. Gerry knew something was very wrong, but in the darkness all he could tell was that he was covered with hydraulic fluid. Canoe next reached over Gerry for the switch that would fire the explosive cutter. He hit it once, then again, and looked out the port. Nothing. The array had broken away neatly from the supporting framework, but it trailed, twisting about, as the *Saucer* raced to the surface. *Merde!* Canoe had known that fancy cutter wasn't going to work. But the danger was past, he hoped. Their trip took only 12 minutes instead of the usual 20. They arrived at the surface with the stern up now that the big weight was gone, and the array dangling limply below. Canoe had explained to Gerry that probably there had been a leak in the hydraulic system. Since the pump was secured, the pressure dropped slowly to the point where the now higher sea pressure forced its way into one line and through the hull. The hydraulic system is an open one, with a reservoir in the cabin. The water had blown back through this, spraying water and oil over them.

Gaston confirmed Canoe's suspicion. He had the culprit in his hand. It was the small actuator that we had added. No one had checked it carefully enough to note that it was a single-acting actuator with the type of seal that could not stand a higher pressure outside. I was surprised that Gaston had not spotted this earlier—he was a most thorough specialist and rarely let such things slip by.

The incident pointed out several things. In our business one has to be extremely careful of the type of equipment used—lives are at stake and even a seemingly minor gear failure can be crucial. We could see that clear, fast thinking was extremely important in such situations. And finally, we saw that the vehicle *Soucoupe* was safely designed and built to be able to recover from possibly catastrophic mishaps in a routine manner.

Canoe was fairly nonchalant, expressing the usual *"c'est la vie scientifique"* and shrugging as if to say, "Oh well, it's all in a day's diving in *La Soucoupe*." But I knew that he must also have felt concerned; he'd made numerous dives—perhaps 50 or 75—over these four months, and this was a job where one couldn't afford to be careless. I think that after this dive Canoe became a bit more cautious. I didn't blame him.

Gerry Assard accepted the incident as part of the normal hazards of going to sea for science. Everyone aboard was impressed with his apparent calmness and his eagerness to make another dive as soon as we were ready again. He deserved another dive, since this one had lasted less than an hour.

On the way home Gaston, Jerry, and Ken mopped out the *Saucer*. The foam berths were soaked—everything was oily and slippery and smelled of hydraulic fluid. Gaston purged the system to remove any corrosive salt water. A new and proper actuator was installed when we got to San Diego and the system was checked over carefully.

Not long after this incident we received a wire from Captain Cousteau stating that the *Saucer* was to be piloted only by an OFRS crew. This was discouraging to Larry and Joe, but I appreciated Captain Cousteau's feeling of responsibility. Canoe's example of fast action in an emergency showed that there was more to piloting than skill of maneuvering control. Our pilots had to wait until *Deepstar* arrived.

The following week we launched five more dives. Gerry Assard finally obtained what looked like some meaningful data on dive 320, which lasted five and a half hours. This was one of the longest dives made with the *Saucer*. On his second dive of the week, he and Canoe waited for several hours on the bottom as one merchant ship after another interfered with the recording. One of the ships we could see, but the other, according to our radar, was at least 18 miles away from the *Saucer*. As that noise faded the saucernauts told us, via the *Shazam* network, that they heard a new noise, which was probably that of a submarine. Finally they gave up and surfaced after three hours and with not a bit of data. On such days, when the sea state was low or nearly calm, the chance of not getting any worthwhile data was high. Usually the ambient sea and wave noise would cover or mask long-range noises of ships that interfered with measurements.

The dives had settled down and both the acoustic and EM

groups were collecting what appeared to be valuable data. They really couldn't tell us much more until the final reductions were performed several months later. They all seemed satisfied. If they were—then we were also.

By the 20th of March the *Saucer*, piloted by Canoe alone, had made 15 dives for USL. We had done all that had been expected and perhaps more. The *Saucer* made it possible for USL engineers and scientists to put some highly diverse and special noise-measuring equipment on board. It had proved to be an extremely stable and satisfactory platform that had no self-noise. To date we knew of no other submersible vehicle that had been used in this way. Both the acoustic and EM scientists believed that they had collected data that would prove significant.

There remained a little over one month to go. We were now a seasoned crew, and ready to try some rougher weather offshore in April.

CHAPTER 10

April Showers in
the Channel Islands

While the USL rig was still in place, we attempted some similar dives for a group of scientists at NEL who were also interested in electromagnetic measurements. After four days of nosing out into a stormy sea we were able to make only one dive. We made this one routinely, in waves 2 to 3 feet high and an increasing wind. Part of the crew were watching television as the nation viewed the first two-manned orbital Gemini flight on March 23—a significant first. The date was a milestone for the *Saucer* on the Westinghouse contract too, as this was dive 330—our 100th dive since November. Our work was less heralded, of course, than the space effort, but consider how similar were portions of the two operations. In both, two men climbed into a small capsule or sphere that protected them from a so-called hostile environment. In one case, men in a sphere were drifting, self propelled, under great pressures and controlled by buoyancies. In the other, they were drifting weightless, controlled by the force of gravity. There were of course differences, for our observer was untrained and needed no special qualification to be a saucernaut other than professional interest and a diving plan.

The celebration for dive 100 of Saucer '65 was highlighted by Little Joe Fordyce, who stood, neatly uniformed, with silver tray and champagne, white napkin on arm, waiting to greet the two returning undersea adventurers. The event was a bright spot in a gloomy, gray, overcast day.

The week turned out to be one of battling the weather and canceling dives, with an end result of two dives instead of five. The following week was little better, even though we shifted our dive sites for the Scripps scientists to the protection of the canyons inside Point La Jolla. We accomplished only three out of six tries. We found that even if we couldn't dive because of bad weather, we expended as much time as for a regular dive. We usually sat and watched the sea, debating whether it was moderating at all, and in the end canceled the dive and arrived back at San Diego two hours later. Our dive quota for March had been fulfilled, but the outlook for April was grim.

One of the more interesting dives we managed to squeeze in when the choppy short swells abated was the one we made for Dr. Carl Hubbs, a marine biologist from Scripps. He had wished for many years to be able to collect a representative sample of fish from the rocky parts of the canyons and the slopes around Point La Jolla. Nets and dredges worked fairly well on even, regular slopes for some fish but were hopeless in rocky areas, where they snagged and where they could not reach in under overhanging ledges. The Scripps scuba divers had been using a sort of poison to help in collecting fish. It was harmless to divers but paralyzing to most small organisms. Of course, the divers only worked to a maximum depth of 200 feet on such missions. Dr. Hubbs wanted specimens from deeper areas. He collaborated with biologists at NEL, who designed and built a giant "slurp gun" to be carried by the *Saucer*. The scuba diver's slurp guns for specimen collecting draw in a large amount of water in a tube and in so doing "slurp" up many small fish otherwise impossible to catch. Our device was similar in the end result, but it was, in fact, more like an underwater vacuum cleaner in appearance. The equipment arrived one afternoon. I could see the look on Gaston's face—oh, no, not another contraption, it seemed to say. But he smiled and said he would try to install the gun. So, while we battled the waves and attempted to get in some regular observation dives, Gaston, Jerry, and Ken doped out the installation of the "fish sucker."

There was a large metal cylinder with a mesh net inside and which also housed a propeller and simple electric trolling motor. This propeller created a suction at one end, where a long section of flexible hose stretched to the mechanical arm of the *Saucer*. The mesh of the net allowed sediment and water to pass through, but collected the animals. The scheme would suck in fish and any floating organisms that the poison had immobilized or killed, thus bringing some of the smaller creatures back for study.

Dr. Hubbs made the trial dive with the fish sucker to see if it was going to work. He picked a spot at 150 meters in Scripps Canyon where he was fairly sure there were fish that he had not been able to get samples of previously. Dr. Hubbs was a tall, heavyset, alert man in his seventies, highly energetic and interested in his work. He had studied the local fish population for many years and looked forward to the improved ways of sampling specimens offered by the *Saucer*. As was true of Dr. Shepard, Dr. Hubbs' age didn't permit the rigors of scuba, but the *Saucer* made it possible for him to see for the first time the areas he knew only from dredge hauls.

About a half gallon of the poison was poured into a plastic bag and the end folded to let the claw close on it. After the *Saucer* was in the water we handed the bag to the diver, who placed it in the open claw and made sure when Canoe closed the jaws that it would stay. This had to be done quickly or we would drift away from our desired launch spot. Usually Earl would allow for some drift and place the ship to windward of the desired dive location. This time our extra procedures took too long and when the *Saucer* was cast off, we had drifted too far.

After a while the *Saucer* crew reported an unfavorable bottom and steep slopes. They had missed the desired spot. We guessed that they were going to proceed up the canyon into flatter ground. About an hour later they reported that the poison had been dropped and all was going well. Dr. Hubbs continued the dive to the usual four-hour limit. I suspect he would have liked to stay longer if Canoe had let him.

As he emerged from the *Saucer* it looked as though he had been slightly cramped in it. Anyone over 6 feet tall had to fold himself somehow. Most of the scientists never complained, because they were too busy and fascinated with what they saw from the port. Dr. Hubbs was no exception. I asked him, "How did you enjoy your first dive, Dr. Hubbs?"

"Fine, fine," he said. "I didn't get to bed last night until late—had a little sniffle. But that dive seems to have cleared it all up."

He went on to describe the dive. It hadn't been wholly successful but certainly worthwhile. When they had reached 150 meters the walls of the canyon were too steep for them to work with the fish sucker. In the rocky areas it looked too rough to place the funnel of the hose and get any suction to suck up fish. After some reconnoitering Canoe remembered a better spot up the canyon where the slopes were more gentle. It took quite a while to move against the current, but when they arrived they found it was a good spot for a trial of the system. Canoe released the poison, which flowed out of the bag slowly, creating a whitish cloud as it mixed with the water. It moved slowly, with a curent of .1 to .2 knot.

The poison, which attacks only the small fish several inches in length, took about 30 to 45 minutes to affect the fish. This poison is a valuable way for the biologist to collect fish since it affects whole assemblages in a small community. It was possible for several timid animals to lurk behind or under a rock unseen even with the *Saucer*. The biologists wanted to gain a clearer idea of the total fish population density and on their *Saucer* dives attempted to get some idea of the number of individual fish. Much of previous conventional collecting from the surface had been nonquantitative. The biologists used the odometer of the *Saucer* to measure distance traveled or, more correctly, amount of water traveled through. The number of organisms and the distance covered establish a basis for estimating population density.

Dr. Hubbs suggested that some improvements be made to the fish sucker before the next dive. More power was needed to pull in larger fish, and the funnel had to be tilted slightly to enable better placement near the fish.

We made an addition to our crew in late March. I had wanted to give everyone some time off, but we were short-handed, with only five of us plus the two OFRS men. A new man, Bob Dunn, joined the team to help with the mechanical problems and maintenance; he was to become part of the group operating *Deepstar* DS-4000. Bob was the first native Californian of our group. He was a trained machinist and also had broad experience in photography, especially underwater work. As he became familiar with the work I was able to ro-tate everyone on a leave schedule. Each man was given a whole week of the remaining five weeks. I even managed to schedule myself for a couple of days off. An operation isn't run-ning smoothly until the boss can walk off for a while—and many times, I've heard, it runs much better without him.

In keeping with his past performance, André arrived just as we were getting ready to go off for two weeks of diving. He had come to relieve Canoe, who hadn't been home in nearly six months.

With these changes, I felt we were ready for the last 25 dives that were scheduled.

Toward the end of the first week in April, Dr. Winterer joined us to make a series of three dives that would take us west of San Nicolas Island to a point about 160 miles at sea.

The weather continued to be uncertain and changeable. One day would be excellent and the next blow up a storm, only to be fine again for diving the following day. It was not the sort of sea weather that I was accustomed to on the East Coast. People who had lived a long time in San Diego said they had never seen such a run of bad, rainy weather.

We left on the following Tuesday night, moving out of San Diego harbor and around Point Loma in a gentle breeze and a partly cloudy sky with a bit of a washed-out moon. At about 0630 I could see the hills and steep slopes of San Clemente rising into a low cloud. We were near the southern end of the island. A squall of rain was moving down that island and parts of it would appear and disappear in the downpour. As we moved up the island it cleared briefly. Dr. Winterer decided to make a dive here, for the weather reports promised nothing good for the islands farther out. At this location we were clearly in the lee of the island and protected from the prevailing northwest wind. As we already knew from our previous San Clemente episodes, the slopes dropped off quickly from the shore. The *Burch Tide* nosed in toward the high cliffs. I couldn't believe my eyes as we came closer—the island was actually green from the last three weeks of rain. It was hardly a luxuriant, rich grass—but it wasn't the brown dirt and rock color we had seen in the fall. Earl approached the beach slowly—closer and closer, until we were less than a ship's length from the rocky cobble beach. Above us the cliffs and steep slopes rose almost vertically to the zenith. As I stood on the stern I could have sworn we were aground "on the prow."

"The depth by the echo sounder is 10 fathoms," Earl announced on the P.A. "Isn't this the place where you wanted to launch the *Saucer*?"

"Roger, Earl, we'll be ready in a few minutes," I replied on the radio.

Jerry Winterer slipped quickly into the *Saucer* and we put it over the stern, which Earl had swung around toward shore. This was the closest in to land we had ever launched. Yet the maximum depth for the *Saucer* lay no more than 500 meters distance offshore. It was in 15 meters of water by the time it was cut loose and the ship was getting really close to shore.

Earl moved as soon as the *Saucer* left the surface.

The *Saucer* proceeded down this steep bank, while Dr. Winterer looked for rock outcrops. He was curious to see if this underwater portion of the island resembled the topography of its terrain above. There is a steep escarpment that runs southwards into and along the San Clemente Rift Valley, going east of Forty Mile Bank. The fault, like many of those in California, is northward trending. Jerry Winterer hoped that it might be possible to get far enough down slope to see the Miocene rock—perhaps even some outcrops of rock earlier in age than Miocene. However, the saucernauts saw nothing but the commonly observed rocks all the way down to 300 meters. The dive's other mission was to investigate the nature of the transport or deposition along the slope. Jerry found no evidence of any strong currents, but there did seem to be considerable downslope movement of the materials along the bottom. A typical slope angle seemed to be about 25 degrees, but it didn't appear to be quite the angle of repose. The geologist usually defines the angle of repose as that angle beyond which sediment begins to move. The divers observed that in the case of burrows made on top of large angular rocks there were indications of the material being spread out toward the downside, giving a very definite impression of the downslope transport of sediments. Nearer the surface too they noted signs of this type of action. As the *Saucer* had descended in shallow water, they found themselves in a veritable forest of kelp. Moving through this kelp into deeper water they noticed that on the other side of the "forest" bits and pieces of detrital kelp were still floating along. This kelp continued most of the way down, suggesting that it is carried down slope. Thus the slope appeared to be one not of deposition but of transport.

The first outcrops of rock occurred around 80 meters, where some of the kelp had hung up and was draped around the rocks. The outcrops ranged from several feet to some 10 feet or more in size—some running lengthwise and others rising vertically from the slope. In between these outcrops were sandy patches with some gravel. "You get the impression," said Jerry, "that the fine materials are running past the larger rocks, something like a pinball machine where the balls run past obstacles."

Where all this material comes from is not known; perhaps it is shelly matter from shallow water or it may be mineral material brought down by the coastal streams. The sample of sand, shell, and gravel that the *Saucer* brought back was most probably volcanic rock. During the dive Jerry looked for indications of geological structures as they descended and then came back up the slope. He could not see any signs of rock outcrops but suspected the bedding plane of the rock would be parallel to the slope they were on. All he observed was large displaced blocks. What was of interest, both going down and coming back up, was a very distinct narrow bench at 80 meters, not more than a few meters wide. Here Jerry saw some round gravel of a size not observed on the rest of the dive. There was an accumulation of some highly rounded boulders up to several feet in diameter, which led him to interpret the bench feature to be an old beach line. This supposition was further substantiated when they returned up slope at a different spot and found the same type of deposits at 80 meters. There were no shells evident, however, for collection and possible geologic dating.

Jerry noted a peculiar kind of smoothing around some of the boulders both on the uphill as well as the downhill side. At first it appeared to be a moat that might have been scoured out by a current, although there was no evidence of currents or current transport. This dive was near the site of a a dive made in the fall, when similar features had been reported. At that time the *Saucer* diver stated that on looking closely he had seen an ocotpus near one of the boulders. Most likely the octopus had been responsible for neatly cleaning his front or back yard. The octopus is known as a careful housekeeper and sometimes builds walls around its house like a good New England farmer.

In summarizing the dive afterwards, Dr. Winterer concluded that the sediment cover on this steep slope was quite thin, perhaps only 2 or 3 feet. It appeared to be gradually slipping down slope and in general appearance was much like the slopes above water on San Clemente Island.

The ship got underway for a point west of San Nicolas. We passed by Wilson Cove in the mid-afternoon. The cove had the same bleak and weathered look as always. A place without trees, it was seasonless and devoid of life. Rounding the northern point we found a medium long swell of 4 or 5 feet. The partly overcast sky and freshening breeze were an ill omen. By early evening we were abeam of San Nicolas Island, which lay about 15 miles to the north. We sat in the wheelhouse and listened to the weather forecast on the marine frequency. It called for storm warnings to the Mexican border, with 20- to 30-knot winds. Any chances of diving were unlikely.

Our dive was to locate a possible site for some deep drilling to be done in the fall. This bank was surrounded by deep water and appeared to be an ideal spot to drill into later in the year. A dive by *Saucer* might find a particular point on the bottom more interesting and valuable than the one selected merely by looking at the chart. Soon after the weather broadcast we all turned in, for the ship was due on station at 0100. I awoke at 0115. I could hear the loud rush of water under the vans and down the center aisle. The ship rolled heavily and spray whipped across the deck between the vans; the antenna wires and halyards whistled. I waded to the deckhouse and up onto the bridge.

The helmsman, an old-time fisherman with years of experience in this area, stood looking at the seas building all the time.

"Don't think you could make a dive here for two-three days most likely," he speculated, squinting out the large windows of the wheelhouse. I agreed. It was bleak and stormy. The lights from the ship enabled us to see the whitecaps churning over. The ship lay in the trough. The wind must have been blowing 25 or 30 knots.

"Where would you suggest we go to get in a lee?" I asked.

"The only place in a wind like this," he said, peering to the northeast and leaning his great bulk on the wheel, "is north of Santa Cruz. I'd reckon that's near 65 miles away."

We certainly weren't going to accomplish anything in this place.

"Sure," I said. "And that'll let us sleep pretty well, won't it?"

"Sure will. We'll have the sea on our stern."

For the rest of the night we ran comfortably downwind and rounded the east end of Santa Cruz through Anacapa Passage just after daybreak. The ship worked its way into Chinese Harbor under the lee of a beautifully green, high, and somewhat forested island. The chart showed it to be 25 miles long by 6 miles wide. Most of it is used for cattle ranching. From where we observed near shore it seemed to get much more rain than the other islands we had seen. Small streams flowed down the slopes and steep cliffs, but where San Clemente had rock and gravel slopes, Santa Cruz was luxuriant in grass and trees. Ahead of us a waterfall fell 50 to 75 feet onto a sand beach. It was a beautiful sight, so unlike most of the rest of this rugged California coast. We ate breakfast in the calm of the harbor, but realized that any diving was out of the question. The heavy rains that made the island a garden spot had produced a muddy runoff that finished the underwater visibility in the harbor. We ran out into Santa Barbara Channel a few miles, still partly protected by the island of Santa Cruz, until Jerry, using the echo sounder, found a bank with a steep side that looked worth diving on.

The dive was made amid rain squalls and under shredded clouds blown aloft by strong winds. The waves ran close together and about 4 feet high. Our newly arrived Bob Dunn was in *Shazam* and had a wet and chilly time. After about two and a half hours the sea had become more choppy and confused by a crosswind; I decided to call the *Saucer* back. When it returned to the surface some 30 minutes later, the crosschop in the sea made the hookup difficult. The timing of the motion of the ship and that of the *Saucer* was critical. As the *Saucer* bobbed around, *Shazam* kept a strain on it to keep it away from the ship's stern, while two of us pulled on the hookup line. I kept watching the waves. Finally the right moment came—I yelled "Now!" Ken dipped the crane down, and the hook snapped home with a solid clank. At the same moment the water beneath the *Saucer* had dropped away, leaving a void. We could feel the whole ship shudder as the 4-ton weight of the *Saucer* accelerated on the crane boom. We prayed that the three shackles on the lifting bridle were sound. Who could guess what the instantaneous loading was on the shackles or how many times this force could be applied? If one of the shackles or the pad eye were to break, it could be disastrous to the *Saucer* and the crew. I could see that in the handling techniques and equipment we were in need of improvements, for our operation was confronting limitations caused by the weather. We could readily understand the reasons for Cousteau's Rule 1: "Avoid the surface—either operate above it or below it." This particular recovery was the nastiest we experienced throughout the program. We had made many recoveries that took a longer time or were more fouled up—but this one yanked the *Saucer* with a shuddering jerk.

The storm was clearing and a fine afternoon developed, but the wind increased, blowing steadily from the north. The *Burch Tide* headed for Port Hueneme and the shelter of a good harbor. The following day we attempted a dive off Anacapa Island east of Santa Cruz. By the time we had found the spot on the echo sounder where Dr. Winterer wanted to start the dive, the short choppy sea seemed too forbidding. I decided to cancel the dive and we returned to the refuge of Port Hueneme. Jerry Winterer departed here, while we waited for our next scientist.

The spring winds blew for the next two days, stirring up the local waters and making them entirely too muddy for diving. Dr. Inman had driven up from La Jolla in order to dive in the canyon at Point Mugu about 8 miles south of Port Hueneme but after two days of trying he could see that the dive would have been a wasted one.

Saturday evening the ship put on a feast and send-off party for Canoe Kientzy on the eve of his return to France. Little Joe prepared some fine steaks, put on his best tablecloth, candles, and good china. Canoe had made 40 dives during the past two months—sometimes two in one day—and a total of 81 dives since the start of the contract. Without him as pilot we could not have achieved the results that we had. In the morning Canoe left by plane for Paris.

The ship stayed in Port Hueneme over the weekend, for on Monday a group from Pacific Missile Range (PMR) were to join us for a trip out to San Nicolas. Part of the time the *Burch Tide* tied up behind the strange-looking contraption called *Cuss I*. This converted vessel had performed the experimental drilling at sea on the test site off Guadalupe Island for Mohole in 1959. It was now being converted for other offshore drilling. The full-size rotary drilling rig aboard the ship was an impressive sight.

On Monday diving seemed possible and although the day was cloudy the sea had calmed down considerably. As we started our week for Pacific Missile Range, I felt as though we were under a great deal of pressure. Here it was nearly the middle of April and the log book showed only four dives completed. Things would have to improve if this contract was to be considered successful.

F. G. Wood, a biologist, made a dive on a bank 4 miles offshore, where he thought there was a chance of seeing a "doll" porpoise. His group had been studying porpoises and training them to perform homing missions, carry pingers, and assist divers in experimental work for the Navy. Some experts thought that porpoises, also called dolphins, could be trained to lead reconnaissance swimmers into enemy harbors using their special "sonar." The doll porpoise was rare and had only once been kept in captivity. Wood wanted to see one in its natural habitat. There had been reports of the presence of these porpoises in this area, although not one had been seen by divers. The *Saucer* dive lasted several hours, but there was not a sign of the doll porpoise. "Woodie" did see a lot of worthwhile invertebrates, so his dive was not in vain.

Our floating home next got underway for San Nicolas Island, where we had three dives planned. The *Burch Tide* arrived at the island about daybreak, gliding along on a nearly flat sea. From the angle of approach I could see the length of the island—about 9 miles—and the fairly gently sloping easterly side, a flat terrace top, and steep cliffs facing north.

This island, like the other six or seven of the offshore group, was most probably connected with the mainland during the Pleistocene glacial age. It is said that elephants roamed San Nicolas and their fossilized remains are preserved in the sand-covered hills of the island. A series of wet and dry cycles created tropical and desert conditions in which all the vegetation perished, finally ending the existence of the elephants. But prehistoric man survived by eating the ever-present abalone. He left ample evidence in the kitchen midden remains of crude tools, and of weapons. In the mid-nineteenth century many Indians lived on the island, until the Russians and the Aleuts came. They killed the entire male population and carried off the women and children. There is an interesting recorded historical account of the "lost woman of San Nicolas." According to this document, one Indian woman managed to hide and stayed after all the rest left. She lived alone for 20 years. She was finally captured and taken off about 1855. Later in the century, a realtor tried to develop the island and staked out lots, but there were no buyers. It became a favorite site for archeologists and geologists until the U.S. Navy took it over for a bombing range, missile-practice range, and offshore station. Like San Clemente it lay barren and treeless, a contrast to Santa Cruz 40 miles away.

Our diver was Lt. John Robert Elzenga from PMR, who had made dive 249 with us in November. We couldn't have asked for a better day. The sun was bright, the air crisp and clear as we launched the *Saucer* in about 80 meters of water. As a geologist, Bob was interested in observing and inspecting old beach terraces that presumably existed a mile or two to the northeast of the island. A paper published in 1950 had mentioned some echo-sounder indications of benches or nips that could have been former low-sea level stands in the geological past. These had been described as being at 170 and 300 feet. Bob was now going to try to inspect and examine the area at a depth of around 90 to 100 meters.

When Bob and André reached the bottom at 80 meters

they saw many large angular rocks 3 to 4 feet large, but none with fresh surfaces; all were well encrusted. The sediment surrounding these boulders was a coarse shelly-looking sand that was light in color. The *Saucer* moved in a NNE direction in search of a bench or terrace.

The *Saucer* cruised along over a flat bottom, leaving behind the large boulders and going over a calcareous, shelly sand. Soon the saucernauts came on an area of hills and gullies, which looked like large ripples that trended north-south and were symmetrical. Bob couldn't see any signs of transport down these gullies and, in fact, saw no indication of current along the bottom. The bottom slope toward deep water was very gentle and after about three-quarters of a mile of steady running, they came to an area of concentrated shell fragments at 100 meters. At this point, the bottom dropped away sharply, but there was unfortunately no well-defined bench usually associated with ancient beach features. The shell was all old and not fresh. Although these may have been some part of a beach, the shells continued down the steep slope to 140 meters, though decreasing in occurrence. Bob expected the shell area to be concentrated. No rock outcrops appeared, but there were some large blocks that may once have had stratification. With a claw André managed to pick up a sample of what looked like typical beach rock. Since beach rock forms only at sea level this fact could be significant. It was of interest to note that the saucernauts experienced a sudden very strong current just as they were going over the edge of the slope. Bob said later, "Suddenly we found ourselves tearing along over the bottom. When we finally managed to slow down and stop by digging the claw into the bottom, the current meter registered 0.6 knots." This occurred at a depth of from 110 to 120 meters, but, strangely, below this area there was no current at all. Among the organisms observed were the usual rockfish, urchins, starfish, sea pens, and flatfish. A interesting observation was the fact that all the flatfish they saw were swimming 4 or 5 feet off the bottom. Normally these fish hide in the sand and have to be prodded to make them move. The dive reached a maximum of 140 meters, and then returned to the surface. Bob felt that he had perhaps found something corresponding to the old beach, but that he needed more information to substantiate his finding.

The *Saucer* was retrieved at 1100 and still had a good charge left in the batteries. I decided we could "try for two" and get in another dive on the other side of the island for Woodie, our porpoise man. Our spirits were high as the ship plowed along through low, choppy waves. Perhaps we could keep this pace and make up lost ground. As the dive proceeded I suddenly had a feeling that all was well and that the rest of the month's dives would be easily accomplished.

That's almost the way it happened. Only one dive in the next two weeks had to be canceled because of rough water. That cancellation was an interesting one, because it was the only time that we ever had to pick up the *Saucer* during launch. The observer was André Rosfelder, a Scripps geologist who wanted to investigate Mugu Canyon at Point Mugu.

Our day started with a series of frustrations. As we started to make a dive in Mugu Canyon, only a few minutes from launch, the PMR control center advised us by radio to move several miles away, for they were starting gunnery practice. We argued that "several miles" put us into deeper water than the *Saucer* was capable of diving in. But, since the gunnery was underway we had no choice but to leave. The dive was scrubbed and Point Dume, some 20 miles south, was selected as the alternative canyon. Everything was prepared. A fresh breeze had been blowing several hours; nevertheless, I wanted to make the dive. The ship moved in close to the rocky point near the head of the canyon. When the *Saucer* went into the water something looked wrong, for it took a steep bow-down angle as it hung on the nylon tag line. Gaston conferred at length with André Laban in French. I suspected that the mercury system was at fault. We waited. By this time the ship had drifted into the trough and was beginning to move toward the shore at an increasing rate. Earl, of course, was helpless, for he didn't dare maneuver with the *Saucer* in the water.

Gaston said, "Pick up the *Soucoupe*."

I had often wondered what we would do if faced with such a situation. The *Saucer* was attached to the crane boom only by a small piece of braided line, with a shackle that joined the snap hook of the 10,000-pound-tensile strength nylon tag line. This rig was intended merely to support the 55 pounds in water weight of the *Saucer* prior to launch. Normally, upon recovery of the *Saucer* the nylon line was run through the large ring of the lifting bridle by the diver and the end fastened to the open automatic hook. In the present situation we were unable to get the lifting ring back into the hook jaws. Pulling on the tag line didn't do any good. I looked up to see that the rocks were now quite close and there wasn't time for experimenting. Nor could we hazard passing the nylon line through its proper reaving on the hook for pickup since the line was all that held the *Saucer* in.

Earl's concerned voice came over the P.A. "You all better hurry up and do something back there." I had been tugging and Ken was trying to work the crane into position, but the *Saucer* was dragging sidewise as the ship, blown by the breeze, slipped in the trough.

Finally, Larry, who was the diver, saw the right moment and with a great lunge pulled the bridle up, slamming the hook jaw shut on the ring. This was an extremely dangerous thing to do, for it was easy to get a hand or arm caught between the end of the crane boom and the hatch of the *Saucer*. Larry saved the day, however. Ken plucked the *Saucer* out and Larry jumped aboard *Shazam*, which had been standing by as Earl moved the ship into deeper water.

Gaston found the fault in the lever that shifted the mercury and repaired it in less than 30 minutes. But by this time the freshening wind had managed to chop up the channel and the water along the shore to a point that made it too rough to launch and recover without great risk. The dive was cancelled. Our day had been one long "fezzle" —as they say in Maine.

The remaining dives came off without a hitch. Dive 350, with Dr. H. W. Menard, was another of the Westinghouse-OFRS 50th-anniversary dives and was made in Scripps Canyon. Then two of the Eric Barham scattering-layer (DSL) observations were performed out in San Diego trough in 700 fathoms at about four in the morning. Finally the last dive on the regular schedule took place in Mugu Canyon. After three or four aborted dives, André Rosfelder managed to have a profitable but not exciting dive. He found the canyon full of fine sediment, which made the visibility very poor. Mugu Canyon was unlike many of the coastal canyons that had now been explored by the *Saucer* and was apparently one of high-sedimentation conditions.

With our last scheduled dive completed, and for the last time on this program, the *Burch Tide* headed south toward Long Beach. We were now quite familiar with the coast, the islands, and this portion of California. Without actually measuring or adding up the ship's log, I guessed we had probably steamed at least 3,000 miles just along the California coast, not including our trip to Baja and San Lucas.

The *Deepstar* team was in a jovial mood. It suddenly dawned on us that we had accomplished our goal and in fact we had done much more. We had made a total of 123 dives, more than expected. As we were approaching Long Beach a call came in over the marine telephone. It was from our bosses in Baltimore—Joe Laing, Ben Moore, and Bill Sparks —who congratulated everyone on getting the job done and described its importance to the company.

Over the next week we had to prepare the *Saucer* for its return to France and remove all the special equipment that had been installed in November. It was time to fold our tents and silently steal away.

CHAPTER 11

One Saucer and a
Bag of Pelican Bones

Pier B, Berth 27, in Long Beach was where everything had started six months earlier. The bulk loader was still grinding away in the background, spraying a fine black soot over everything. Little had changed. In the distance the birdlike pumping jacks were pecking away in the monotonous rhythm as they pumped oil out or seawater back in to keep Long Beach from sinking any more. Our return was triumphant, even if without fanfare.

On the way from Mugu Canyon, Gaston and Jerry had started stripping equipment from the *Saucer*. The underwater telephone, temperature sensor, current meter, CB radio, special penetrator, and similar objects all came off. Weights were shifted and *La Soucoupe* returned to its original condition.

It was now the 29th of April and although our Baltimore office had found several potential commercial customers for a few more days' diving, Captain Cousteau had firmly requested the *Saucer*'s return. He must have it, he said, on May 8, to make an important dive off Monaco as part of the site survey for the placement of his experimental undersea living quarters, *Conshelf III*. In Baltimore, Tom Horton and Fred Willett had been making arrangements to get a MATS C-124 Cargomaster within several days. So far there were none available. We had to wait.

The least we could do was to try a couple of orientation dives for our new team members. During the last week of diving, Ron Church had been hired on the team as a potential *Deepstar* pilot. Ron was familiar with routine procedures from his visit to San Lucas as a free-lance photographer. Now both he and Bob Dunn wanted a dive. Also, in the last weeks of the contract we had acquired another team member, who was to be our onshore liaison and business manager. This was Fred Bagnall, a former UDT diver and business major in college. Fred was helping with the return shipment of the *Saucer* as well as preparing the way for *Deepstar*, which was now only a few months away.

The *Burch Tide* crew agreed to take the ship out in shallow water off Long Beach for a dive or two. When we got out into the harbor we found ourselves "thick-a-fog," with all ships anchored and many hooting, but unseen. We suspected that the fog might last all day. The skipper consulted the chart and pointed to a spot in the edge of the outer harbor where there was a depth of 50 feet. He thought we could work there safely. I told Ron, Bob, and Fred this was our only choice since trying to go outside would be too slow. The water looked quite dirty, so it was doubtful if they'd see much. The ship anchored well out of the way of any traffic. When it came time for the selection of divers, André said he could take both Ron and Bob. I hadn't realized that three could get into the *Saucer*. Gaston explained that, since they had lightened it considerably and since André was no heavyweight, the

Saucer could take a third person.

"One sits horseback way on the water ballast tank," said André.

Dive 354 lasted an hour and a half, while Ron was given a chance to try the *Saucer* controls and get the feel of the quick maneuvering ability. On his return he remarked, as Larry and Joe had on their first dives, how delicate the *Saucer* was and how easy to overcontrol.

For the final dive, 355, Fred Bagnall and I went along to maintain the same ballast. Ron had said the visibility was surprisingly good—for a harbor like Long Beach. The *Saucer* left the surface amid a brightening overhead but dense fog around. Immediately I was impressed with the yellowish light that give way to a lime-green color in the water. On the surface I guessed the visibility to be a foot or two and did not expect any light at all under water. On the contrary it was amply bright there and at times we could see nearly 6 feet ahead— not bad for a dirty harbor. I started by sitting "horseback style" astride the tank. As André tipped the *Saucer* bow down, at 30 degrees I could grab the hatch assembly to hold on. Later I switched with Fred and had a chance to look closely at a number of organisms happily pursuing their activities in the water and on the bottom. Even in apparently polluted harbors life goes on regardless.

By the 1st of May we received an official statement from the MATS headquarters that they could not supply a plane for several weeks. All aircraft, even some commercial planes, had been diverted to the Dominican Republic crisis. Our reason for using the military aircraft had, of course, been to save money on the contract, which was a Navy contract, but there was no reason why the *Saucer* couldn't return via commercial planes. The various customer groups would have to share the air expense. As far as Fred Willett knew, only one commercial aircraft could easily accommodate the *Saucer*. This was a CL-44 made by Canadair for Flying Tigers—Seaboard Air. Instead of a large double-cargo door on the side it had a tail section that could swing open with a ten-foot inside diameter horizontally. Unfortunately, the vertical clearance was a few inches too small.

Through the Flying Tigers office, Fred Bagnall made arrangements for a plane to arrive no later than May 4 while on the ship the welders cut the *Saucer* cradle from the ship. The next morning a large yellow crane arrived, reached gently over the high dock, and picked up the small yellow *Saucer*. The other bits and pieces of tools, spare parts, and auxiliary support equipment that had come with the *Saucer* were loaded onto a waiting flatbed truck. With a fond farewell, the *Burch Tide* crew waved good-bye to the *Saucer*. The spot where it had stood looked vacant and gaping.

Gaston had long known he must ride with the *Saucer* on its return to watch and guard it. Jerry volunteered to go along as far as New York, to make sure the transfer there from Flying Tigers to Seaboard Air was done correctly. André had elected to return by passenger plane, in order to avoid the roar and din of the cargo type.

The team decided to give our pilots and mechanic an expression of our thanks for their hard work and help in completing the job. Both André and Canoe were interested in a print of the film, *A Thousand Feet Deep for Science*, that Joe and Ron had put together showing the *Saucer* operation. Gaston had been pricing movie cameras to replace his tired and cranky one. Joe Thompson had hinted that Gaston should wait before buying one. Nevertheless, he was taken by surprise when Jerry handed him a supermarket shopping bag, saying, "Your groceries, Gaston, for your trip home."

"For me?" Gaston fumbled at the wrappings. He was visibly overwhelmed when he got to the box that was marked Nikkorex Zoom 8mm-Camera. I had rarely seen Gaston at a loss for words, either in French or English—but he was on this occasion.

The *Saucer* departed for Compton, where at the local Westinghouse plant we had arranged to modify the cradle to enable the *Saucer* to go aboard the CL-44. A special frame was made that was several inches lower and still strong enough to support the 4 tons of the *Saucer*. This meant that the *Saucer* would have to slide along instead of rolling on its normal cradle wheels. Later a long trailer truck took the *Saucer* aboard and began its trek to Los Angeles airport.

We found, as we had suspected, that the forklift used by Flying Tigers had forks too short to reach under the cradle and pick up the *Saucer*. Fred made a quick call to the crane company. They thought that one of the large cranes might be available within hours. It was afternoon by this time. Everything else was off-loaded and placed on the dock of the warehouse. The plane was to arrive the next morning. We waited —and waited. I had time to form an opinion of the loading of air freight. Crates and cartons marked "Fragile," "Glass," or "Scientific Instruments" were tossed, jostled, and heaved about like so many sacks of meal. We watched a forklift that was moving crates give one push too many. A large crate toppled over the edge of the dock, falling about 4 feet with a splintering crash. The operator stopped and jumped down to inspect the partly open crate. He stuffed the parts that had fallen out back in, pounded on the top, and replaced the crate on the dock. I hoped the handling of the *Saucer* would be more gentle.

As the last gleam of a red sun disappeared, the crane arrived, lumbering slowly across the airport expanse. Under the spotlights it picked up the *Saucer* off the flatbed truck and placed it in the waiting arms of the largest forklift available. The forklift had been unable to reach the *Saucer* while it was on the truck. Now it sat balanced and safely held. The forklift hoisted everything up the 9 or 10 feet to the cargo deck. I couldn't imagine the 4-ton *Saucer* going so high on a forklift. "Wait and see" was the password.

Gaston loaded a number of the special pieces of gear into the *Saucer*, where they would be safer than in crates. This equipment became part of the *Saucer* shipment and thus, for French customs, it was "scientific equipment." Suddenly there appeared a "scientific hi-fi" and some "scientific records," and other items that the Frenchmen had procured. On *Saucer* '64, when it was returned to France, they had collected a number of shells—no doubt some were André's—and after several days of being closed up inside the *Saucer* these came to the attention of the curious customs inspectors. One whiff and they declined to look any further. Gaston's collected mementos of the USA and Mexico also included a complete sampling of every seed that he and André could find. They had taken long walks off in the wilds to gather seeds and samples of plants to take to France for cultivation.

Several days earlier André had made a trip to a local super-market to buy a sampling of different kinds of American dog food. He had at least one of every brand, so that his dog could try "imported" foods. These cans were passed into the *Saucer* and a bilge full of dog food went beneath the seats.

The next day the whole team was at the airport. Jerry and Gaston had their bags in hand ready to fly the cargo route to New York. The plane arrived around noon. The *Saucer* went in first although there was already some cargo inside. There seemed to be no more than an inch to spare in both directions. The forklift operator, vastly more skilled than the one I'd seen the day before, took the *Saucer,* lifted it, aimed it, and neatly slid it into the open tail while a helper directed. With a small electric winch and some things that looked like skate boards, the loading crew efficiently slid the *Saucer* in about 40 feet to the middle of the plane. Here they secured it to the deck with numerous tie-downs. The strains in landing and takeoff were extremely great, so special attention was given to properly se-curing the *Saucer* from all angles.

Next were the boxes, crates, tins, and gear that went with the shipment. The total weight had come to 12,640 pounds. Of this, the *Saucer* accounted for approximately 8,300 pounds. What of all the rest, what was it? I glanced over the open crates. Old batteries, the ascent weights we didn't use, some oil, one more emergency weight, some other heavy objects, and all the spares. Then I saw a plastic bag taking up several cubic feet—it had André's cherished pelican bones and sea-shells! I had forgotten these weirdly shaped, white, parched pieces of old pelicans—but André hadn't.

As the CL-44 gunned the engines at the end of the runway

and struggled into the air in a long, slow, gradual climb, I thought: Of the thousands of people at Los Angeles Airport that day, who would imagine that that plane contained a *Saucer* and a bag of pelican bones?

Suggested Submersible Reading

Anderson, F. J. *Submarines, Submariners, Submarining: A Bibliography*. Hamden, Conn.: Shoe String Press, 1963.

Beebe, W. *Half-Mile Down*. New York: Duell, Sloan and Pearce, 1951.

Cousteau, J.-Y. "The Diving Saucer Takes to the Deep," *National Geographic*, April 1960.

Cousteau, J.-Y., and Dugan, J. *The Living Sea*. New York: Harper Bros., 1963.

Cousteau, J.-Y., and Dugan, J. *World Without Sun*. New York: Harper and Row, 1964.

Duggan, James; Cowen, Robert C.; Barada, Bill; Marden, Luis; and Crum, Richard M. *World Beneath the Sea*. Washington, D.C.: National Geographic Society, 1967.

Houot, G. S., and Willm, P. H. *2,000 Fathoms Down*. New York: E. P. Dutton & Co., 1955.

Interagency Committee on Oceanography. *Deep Research Vehicles*. Washington, D.C.: ICO, 1966. (Publication 18)

Keach, D. L. "Down to *Thresher* by Bathyscaphe," *National Geographic*, 1964.

Lake, Simon P. *The Autobiography of Simon Lake*. New York: D. Appleton-Century, 1938.

Piccard, Auguste. *Earth, Sky and Sea*. New York: Oxford University Press, 1956.

Piccard, J., and Dietz, R. S. *Seven Miles Down*. New York: G. P. Putnam & Sons, 1960.

Shepard, F. P., and Church, R. *Undersea Exploration by Diving Saucer*. San Diego County, Calif.: Community Educational Resources Production, Department of Education, 1964.

Shepard, F. P., and Dill, R. F. *Submarine Canyons*. New York: Rand McNally, 1966.

Tailliez, P. *Aquarius*. Paris, France: Editions France, Empire, 1961.

Terry, R. D. *The Deep Submersible*. North Hollywood, Calif.: Western Periodicals Co., 1966.